Menya

*An
End of
Life Story*

Menya

An
End of
Life Story

Morris Wolfe

grubstreet books

National Library of Canada Cataloguing in Publication
Wolfe, Morris
Menya : an end of life story / Morris Wolfe.
ISBN 0-9689737-2-8
1. Wolfe, Menya--Health. 2. Breast--Cancer--Patients--Biography.
3. Terminal care. I. Title.
RC280.B8W645 2003   362.1'9699449'0092   C2002-905819-8

PUBLISHED BY

grubstreet books
1 Humbercrest Boulevard
Toronto, Ontario, Canada M6S 4K6
info@grubstreetbooks.ca · (416) 766-0340

PRINTED AND BOUND IN CANADA BY

Coach House Printing

BOOK AND COVER DESIGN BY

Ben Wolfe Design
ben@benwolfedesign.com

*This book was designed in Adobe InDesign 2.0. The type is
Adobe Jenson Pro, a revival of a face created by Venetian printer
(and student of Gutenberg) Nicolas Jenson in 1470. Jenson's face had
no italic; modern designer Robert Slimbach paired it with an italic
created by calligrapher Ludovico degli Arrighi in the 1520s.*

*The Celtic knot that begins each chapter was extracted from a
batik design on one of Menya's favourite pieces of clothing,
an idea suggested by the memorial banners created from
Menya's personal effects by Linda McKague van Will.*

*My daughter Menya died on February 13, 2001,
at the age of thirty-six after an almost five-year struggle
with metastatic breast cancer. She did not go gently
into that good night. This little book is dedicated
to the fifty or so family members, friends, volunteers
and professionals who cared for her, mostly
at home, during her last months.*

CONTENTS

INTRODUCTION
by June Callwood

THE STORY OF MENYA'S DEATH, as recounted by her grieving father and the dozens of people who loved and tended her through months of an exceedingly difficult end-of-life, is set out calmly in this small book. In an almost matter-of-fact tone, common in those who postpone weeping, it portrays the mundane chores, the appalling crises, the beatitudes found when caring for someone dying, in this case, exacerbated because cancer had blasted not only Menya Wolfe's brain but sometimes her vibrant personality as well.

The infrastructure of the book is the irreducible majesty of the palliative care experience for everyone involved in it. The care team, which included a very fine core of volunteers from Trinity Home Hospice, writes of the privilege of being close to Menya through those months when she raged against death, of the pure pleasure that swept the room when she laughed, of their profound admiration for the depths of determination and fierce courage they saw in her struggle, of the reservoirs of patience and empathy they found within themselves.

For those entering for the first time into caring for someone who is dying, there is much practical help here. An astonishing amount of palliative care is based on common sense, intuition and a few tricks of the trade. Small acts, such as giving a foot massage or a shampoo or finding the right thing to say, are sturdy bridges that allow caregiver and care-receiver to mingle in a transported state where it is not clear which is which. Most importantly, the unspoken message throughout is teamwork—people putting aside their differences to give one another support and praise.

All deaths diminish the human pool, as the poet said. Over time each loss revives memories of all other losses and the tears at the funeral are for every other loved one who is gone, as well as for one's bereft self. For instance, when parents die, there goes one's childhood history; no one else knows it, and it is lonely uncertain work to revisit patches of it alone. All deaths are highway robberies, and the most painful of all is the death of one's child. People say that time heals even that grief. It does, and it doesn't. Not by a long shot. Morris Wolfe keeps his suffering to himself, but it is writ plain between the lines of this moving tribute to his glorious, gifted young daughter and all those who loved her.

The hospice movement which is sweeping Canada grew out of certain knowledge that death may not be preventable but it can be softened by acts of gentle kindness. It is not only the very sick person who is the recipient of the spiritual peace which intermittently accompanies skilled and generous palliative care. Care-givers find themselves deeply and forever changed in ways that sweeten all other relationships. Being in the environment of an imminent death has a way of clarifying priorities. The detritus of a lifetime—unresolved feuds, bitter memories, chronic irritations—wash out to the sea. The price of this epiphany is peanuts: it is merely hours of toil and beauty.

A continuity runs through all end-of-life stories I have read, and written. It is this: that dying is hard work for everyone, fraught with surprises; that the correct decision to respect the wishes of the dying person always admits an element of tyranny; that care-givers experience moments of profound wonder that stir them to their souls; and when it ends, a culmination both dreaded and, eventually, secretly, hoped-for, they are left with a sense of inner unity that will quietly glow for the rest of their lives. This book is about a tragic death but, in many ways, it is a celebration of life.

CHAPTER ONE
April 1996 – July 2000

I N THE SPRING OF 1995, my daughter Menya, who
was then thirty, moved to England. She did so eager-
ly. She was completing her master's thesis in Museum
Studies at the University of Toronto, looking for a job in
her field, and, not least, hoping to meet the right man. She
was successful on all counts. She finished her thesis, found
a job in London restoring artifacts for an antiquities dealer,
and began living with a man named Pete. He came home
with her that Christmas to meet family and friends.

Late one afternoon in mid-April of 1996, Pete called to
tell us that Menya had been diagnosed with inflammatory
breast cancer (IBC), a rare and deadly form of the disease.
She herself was too distraught to come to the phone. All

I remember of the rest of that day was a feeling of dread that took up residence in the pit of my stomach. Something awful was happening to one of my children and there was almost nothing I could do. I spent the next day trying to learn what I could about IBC. What I learned wasn't reassuring: the average life expectancy of a woman diagnosed with IBC was eighteen months.

Over the next few days, Menya exchanged e-mails with family and friends, as she decided what to do. (As something of a Luddite, I had only recently and reluctantly begun using e-mail. Now, suddenly, it was a godsend. Family members and close friends could share information quickly, without repetition, and without running up large phone bills.) Menya couldn't decide whether to return to Canada for treatment. Pete made the decision for both of them; he would give up his job, rent out his house and come with her.

Prior to her diagnosis, Menya's e-mail messages had ended with this ironic postscript:

The golf links lie so near the mill
That nearly every day
The working children can look out
And see the men at play.

She now replaced it with the words,

> *Ever has it been that love*
> *knows not its own depth*
> *until the hour of separation.*

2

MENYA AND PETE ARRIVED back in Canada in early May of 1996. They stayed with me until an apartment became available in the same co-op. (Menya's mother, Carla, and I are divorced.) Her general practitioner in Toronto had arranged for her to see the appropriate specialists. In consultation with them, she decided on a treatment plan. She would undergo six months of intensive chemotherapy followed by a modified radical mastectomy, which removes the breast but leaves the woman's chest muscles intact. Three weeks into chemo, she lost her waist-length hair. A month later, her white cell count fell dangerously low. The chemo was adjusted.

The pathologist's report following her mastectomy

couldn't have been better. Menya's breast tissue and lymph nodes showed no evidence of cancer. The chemo had done its job. We all took a deep breath. As an added precaution, she underwent five weeks of radiation to her chest wall and lymph nodes and began taking the hormone Tamoxifen.

It took Menya a few months to get her strength back. She began swimming and going to yoga classes; she upgraded her computer skills and took on some freelance assignments. Pete had found a job shortly after their arrival, writing software for a computer company. Because so little information was available about IBC, Menya and Pete set up an internet mailing list for women and their caregivers to share information and stories.

They became engaged on New Year's Eve, 1997, and scheduled their wedding for the following October. But ten days before the wedding, Menya learned that the cancer was back. She'd been feeling fuzzy-headed and had gone for a scan that revealed the cancer had metastasized to the left parietal lobe of her brain. Metastases of inflammatory breast cancer are usually found in the lungs, bones, liver, and occasionally the brain. And brain tumours are far more difficult to treat because of the 'blood-brain barrier,' which most drugs can't penetrate.

Menya and Pete went ahead with the wedding—a lovely affair—followed by a honeymoon in Jamaica. Menya was given a steroid, Decadron, to keep her brain swelling down. But Decadron can have awful side effects, both physical and psychological. Pete and Menya weren't prepared for the intensity of these—bloating and severe mood swings. Without brain surgery, the odds of Menya surviving until their first anniversary were slim. But before that could happen, she had to undergo an MRI to see if the cancer was operable. That depended on its location and whether it was a single tumour or a cluster.

It was operable. In late October of 1997, Menya underwent surgery to remove the growth. The surgeon kept her awake throughout the operation; by talking to her, he could ensure that the use of her right arm and leg were being minimally affected. The procedure went well; the surgeon was optimistic. Eighty per cent of operable metastatic brain tumours do not recur, he told us.

Menya was released three days later, but on her first morning at home, she woke with a swollen right leg. She had developed a blood clot. That meant more time in hospital and being put on a blood thinner. As soon as her incision had healed sufficiently, she underwent a week of whole brain radiation, which resulted in extreme fatigue. She lost

*Menya in her early twenties; in England before her cancer
was diagnosed; and during the years of her illness*

her hair again. (The 'new' hair was growing in curly.) By now she had acquired a number of hats and wigs. She'd even appeared on TV as a breast cancer survivor having a makeover.

Once again it took several months for Menya to get her strength back. She and Pete took some short trips—to Niagara Falls and to Montreal, for instance. By the spring of 1998, although it was clear that she'd lost some use of her right hand, she felt well enough to join a dragon boat team of breast cancer survivors called Dragons Abreast and to take on some part-time computer assignments again.

That summer Pete came into enough money to put a down payment on a house in the east end of Toronto. Two of the major selling points of the house were the cathedral ceiling in the master bedroom and a jacuzzi in the large upstairs bathroom. That the jacuzzi leaked into the dining room below didn't matter. It was a useful distraction. Menya talked about having a garden, something she'd never had.

The day before they moved into their house, they learned that Menya's brain tumour was back—in exactly the same location. She'd been having mild seizures— bands of pressure, twitching, and paralysis in her right arm, accompanied by a feeling of disorientation. As a result of this, she was now also on Dilantin, an anti-seizure medication. Because her original surgeon was reluctant to operate again (a second surgery would inevitably result in more disability), Menya opted for stereotactic radiosurgery ('gamma knife' surgery), a relatively new, non-invasive procedure. It involved a single, focused blast of radiation which, in ninety-five per cent of cases, we were told, halted the growth of tumours for a year or two. The one-day procedure meant having a metal frame screwed to her head, having multiple scans done, and then waiting for doctors to determine the precise doses and angles needed to do maximum damage to the tumour and minimal damage to the brain around it. Once they were ready, the tumour was zapped. But within a few months, it was back.

From the beginning Menya had insisted on being in charge of choosing between and among treatment options. Her feistiness and tenacity, which had not always been easy for family and friends to deal with, made her a powerful advocate on her own behalf. She knew her way around libraries and the internet. She was 'up' on all the standard treatments; and was keeping up with research still in the experimental stage. She discussed various options with her medical, radiation and surgical oncologists, fired those she wasn't comfortable with, sought additional opinions, and then decided what to do.

Studies, for example, showed that Thalidomide had been used in Germany with modest success in slowing the growth of advanced cancers. Menya and her medical oncologist, John Blondal, with whom she and Pete had established a warm bond, decided it was worth a try. Dr. John, as he came to be called, obtained permission from the federal government to import and use the drug. Menya began taking escalating doses of Thalidomide in December 1998. At first the tumour shrank a bit, then it began to grow again. An MRI in early January showed the tumour had grown by fifty per cent since October.

Menya decided to undergo invasive surgery for a second time. She found a surgeon willing to operate, and again was kept awake during the operation. In an e-mail to family and friends, Pete reported that the surgery had gone well. But he added, "The doctor thinks he got everything without causing collateral damage, but bear in mind that all brain surgeons have egos the size of, say, Jupiter.... Menya's feeling as though someone bashed her skull in and poked around inside. It's going to be like that for a couple of days." A week later, she was feeling better. But an MRI in March showed 'enhancement'—a new-to-us euphemism for growth.

In mid-April, on the third anniversary of her diagnosis, Pete and Menya held an 'Alive and Kicking Party'. In May they went to Cuba for a brief holiday. While there, Menya had a seizure. On their return, she went back on Dilantin. They learned that an MRI taken just before they'd left showed 'increased enhancement.' Menya turned to chemo again, this time to high doses of Methotrexate. Despite several bi-weekly doses of the drug, which required hospitalization, the tumour continued to grow. She stopped Methotrexate and went back on the modified cocktail that had worked prior to her mastectomy.

Pete kept thinking of ways to keep their—and others'—spirits up. He announced that because Menya was about to lose her hair for a third time, they were going to have a head shaving party. He would shave his head too. Those who weren't prepared to shave their heads had to make a $10 donation to breast cancer research.

An MRI in September showed further growth. The old cocktail no longer worked. Menya and Dr. John decided to switch to Temodal, a new 'wonder' drug. But Temodal was for primary brain tumours. No one knew whether it worked on tumours that had metastasized to the brain. Surgery remained an alternative, but the risk of even more neurological damage was high. As a result of the earlier surgeries, Menya already had a pronounced limp in her right leg, was walking with a cane, and had lost much of the use of her right hand.

It was possible, Pete and Menya now learned, that what was showing on her MRI consisted of dead tissue or necrosis, the result of radiation. Menya leapt at that interpretation. In December, there was a slight improvement in her symptoms. An MRI revealed no new growth. Another test suggested that, yes, there might no longer be a tumour there and that what was there might be necrosis. Menya stopped treatment and began using the 'c' word—'cured.' She and Pete took some time to absorb what was happening. In a mid-December message, they wrote, "We've been too busy recovering to get around to mundane things like Christmas cards."

Early in the new year, Menya posted a letter on the IBC web site she and Pete had just established. (The mailing list had been so successful that they'd expanded it into a site of its own.) "It was days before Christmas," she wrote, "and I had gone from believing the tumour was resistant to everything and that I was going to die, to finding I was free of disease. It was a hard shift to make.... I had almost lost hope, and had to relearn to dream. There were a lot of sleepless nights as my mind made the adjustment. The physical disabilities are still there. I have limited use of my right hand, a pronounced limp, and can only walk a few blocks.... I want to play the harp again, to work with glass and metal, to race in the dragon boat, to ride a bike. If I stay well, I'll have time to relearn some of those things."*

Menya concluded her letter on the web site by saying, "I want everyone to know that there is always hope, that there are survivors. Making contact with an IBC survivor made a huge difference to me when I was diagnosed and feeling overwhelmed.... It was the hope that [we could] do the same that led Pete and me to create first the IBC mailing list and now this web site." That turned out to be Menya's first, and last, entry on the site.

---

* In her mid-teens, Menya had joined SCA (the Society for Creative Anachronism) which celebrates the life and culture of the Middle Ages. Her interests in arts and crafts, music, literature, theatre, dance, anthropology, archaeology and medieval history all came together in the SCA, which became her second family. Not unlike her first family, it was somewhat nerdy. In the mid-eighties, with the help of a fellow SCA member, Menya built a lap harp and taught herself to play it. She even earned a bit of money busking, singing mostly traditional songs and occasionally performing songs she herself had written.

3

IT WAS NOW FEBRUARY OF 2000, almost four years since her original diagnosis. Her MRI remained unchanged but her symptoms were worse. She wanted—needed—to believe that she was cured or, at worst, had a chronic illness and, like people living with AIDS, could stay alive by moving from one experimental drug or combination of drugs to another. By April, her symptoms were a lot worse, and she was having frequent seizures. An MRI in May revealed that the tumour had doubled in size since February and that her brain was showing extensive swelling.

Menya had few choices remaining. A body can absorb only so much chemo and radiation, and she was nearing those limits. She chose to undergo surgery again, this time accompanied by photodynamic therapy, another new treatment that involved being injected with a photosensitizing drug a day before surgery. The drug is activated during the operation, and when it works, it destroys any remaining cancer cells. This time Menya would be under general anaesthetic. Although she knew she would suffer further neurological damage, would need to avoid natural light for a few weeks, and would have to go back on Decadron, she decided to proceed. It was her last hope. A scan in July, a month after the surgery, showed rapid tumour growth and brain swelling. She went back on Temodal. Her symptoms continued to worsen.

CHAPTER TWO

August 2000 – October 2000

THE WORD 'PALLIATIVE' entered the English language in the fifteenth century. For Samuel Johnson, the word was synonymous with 'compassion.' "The cure for the greatest part of human miseries," he writes in his wonderful dictionary (1755), "is not radical, but palliative." Johnson was, of course, referring to the human condition, not to medicine, which in those days could offer little more than compassion. Modern medicine can do much more, but it too has limits. Eventually, we will all die. Palliative care has come to mean the work of professionals and volunteers who devote themselves to improving the quality of life of those who are dying. The word 'hospice,' in the sense of a home for the sick and destitute, didn't enter the language until the end of the nineteenth century. With its suggestion of 'hospital' or 'hospitality,' its connotations seem softer.

In early August, Menya and Pete contacted the Hospice Palliative Care Network (HPCNET), a pilot project in Toronto, to learn about the services available. Menya hated the word 'palliative'—to her it meant failure and surrender. She was willing to accept some of the services they could provide but wouldn't allow the word to be spoken in her presence. She quickly fired two psycho-social workers. They wanted to talk about death and dying; she didn't. Still, by the last week of August, a homemaker was coming to the house two hours a day; a bath lift had been installed; a hospital bed had been set up in the guest room upstairs; and a family friend, Randi Helmers, had been hired to come in half days, five days a week. As well, a Victorian Order of Nurses (VON) nurse continued to make daily visits. This routine allowed Pete to go to work for a few hours a day. He'd return around 2 p.m. and take over as caregiver from then until the next morning.

In an e-mail dated August 25, Pete informed the immediate circle of family and friends: "Menya has been very tired, her right arm and leg have been weaker, she's been having more seizures, and she has occasional problems with memory and speech.... [She] has another scan in about three weeks and then we have to decide whether to continue or not. If she stops temadol, there isn't anything else out there that shows enough promise to be worth the side effects, especially given her low tolerance for Decadron."

Ten days later, because her symptoms were worse, Pete took her to the hospital. A scan showed that the tumour was growing out of control. The doctors said there was nothing more they could do. Menya was now in palliative care, whether she liked it or not. Pete wrote that "although nobody can give an accurate prognosis, the feeling is that she has weeks rather than months to live." That's what the doctors had said or implied, with the exception of one doctor who thought Menya might have another six months.

Pete now shared the news with subscribers to the IBC web site. In response, he and Menya were flooded with e-mails, mostly from people they'd never met. A woman from Colorado wrote, "I hope you both realize how much you've given to us all. You will never know us, but we feel as if we know you. We are saddened by the way things are turning out for Menya."

Menya's thirty-sixth birthday, on September 14, was rapidly approaching. She knew it would be her last. She wanted to celebrate it surrounded by as many of the people she loved as possible. The party had been scheduled for Saturday September 16, but her condition was deteriorating so rapidly that we moved the date up one week. What could have been a maudlin affair, wasn't. About fifty people visited the house that afternoon and evening. Menya greeted her guests warmly. There was a lot of singing and laughter and good food and drink. By the end of the evening a whole coffee table was covered with a mound of the best in chocolate—Godiva, Thornton's Dark Ginger, Green and Black's, etc.—gifts for our ailing chocoholic.

Mostly we shared Menya anecdotes. I told the story of her dirty word collection. Guests would come to visit and Menya, who might have been eight at the time, would sweetly ask if they wanted to see her dirty word collection. Their wary 'okay' would result in their being handed an envelope, which, when opened, contained words like 'dirt,' 'filth,' 'grime' and 'muck.' A long-time friend, Gunnar, told of an older Menya's mischief-making. She'd stand on a beach in a bikini and tell men she had a birthmark in a place they couldn't see. But for five dollars, she offered to show it to them. (It was on the bottom of her right foot.) Menya sometimes claimed to have paid her way through university this way.

Two of the guests that evening were John Blondal, Menya's chemotherapy oncologist, and his wife, Grace. Menya, Pete and the Blondals had become friends. Normally, when a patient stops chemo, the oncologist moves on; there's nothing more for him or her to do. The family doctor or a specialist in palliative care takes over. At Menya's request, Dr. John had agreed to make regular visits, although more as a friend than as a doctor. He'd been away on holiday when Menya decided to stop treatment and she worried that she'd disappointed him in doing so. A few days after the party, he sent her a note. The notion that she had let him down, he wrote, was "a bloody irony, given that I and the medical profession…have failed you. It is a sad reflection on the lack of progress in this field that the same disease that struck my mother in 1959, can at the turn of the century still do such damage…. I am better for having been your doctor and friend."

Not long after the party, while she could still participate, we made funeral plans. Menya wanted her remains buried in Castleton, a small town about hundred miles east of Toronto. Her maternal grandmother and a favourite uncle are buried there. Menya had been named after my maternal grandmother, who was gassed in Auschwitz. I'd assumed Menya would want to be cremated, but one of her friends told me she'd heard Menya say she couldn't bear the thought of cremation because of how her great grandmother's body had been disposed of. She wanted to be buried in a biodegradable cardboard box; to have a memorial service after her death; to have something written about her; to have the Fauré *Requiem* performed in her honour; and to have a charitable foundation established in her name to raise money for research into IBC.

The first three things were easy to agree to. The fourth would take time, but could be managed. (Menya's sister, Jen, and her brother-in-law, Brad, are choral conductors at a U.S. college.) The fifth request, establishing a foundation (no easy matter), had far more to do with vanity than with real need. A foundation devoted in part to IBC research already exists (Saunders-Matthey). Pete told Menya we would do everything we could to fulfil her wishes. We agreed among ourselves that we would invite people to make donations to Saunders-Matthey and Trinity Home Hospice.

I was consoling myself by taking long walks along the Humber River, not far from where I live—watching nature take its course. I was fascinated by salmon swimming upstream, struggling to fling themselves over a low dam, to return to where they were born, in order to spawn and die. The river was low that fall and salmon were getting trapped in the shallow water. I was moved to tears one afternoon as I watched some teenage boys lift trapped salmon, carry them to the top of the dam, and send them on their way.

2 🐉

PETE CONTINUED TO KEEP everyone informed. "She can't use the stairs and walking about is quite difficult," he wrote on September 24. (A stair lift had been installed a couple of days earlier and Menya was now using a wheelchair to get around.) "Her short term memory is getting worse and it's harder for her to find words…. Today was especially bad. She couldn't figure out how to use the phone…. Later she [managed to walk] from the back bedroom to the front, and the stress made her vomit." Pete added that he was feeling overwhelmed and needed to shift more of the load to others.

He arranged for June Galbraith, one of the co-ordinators at Trinity Home Hospice (THH), to do a needs assessment. Menya refused to see her or even to allow her in the house; if Pete wanted to talk to her, he could do so on the front porch. They met on September 29. Pete explained that Menya didn't want anyone other than himself looking after her; furthermore, she didn't think he needed additional help. She'd accepted the help of the homemaker and the von. And she was particularly enjoying having Randi around. When she felt well enough, the two of them would sing old English, Irish, and Scottish folk songs—the bawdier the better—Randi plucking her ukelele, and Menya playing her harp with one hand. But she continued to want Pete to be there for her twenty-four hours a day and couldn't accept that that wasn't possible.

Randi was feeling her way, trying to make things easier for Menya. Her attempts didn't always work. She thought, for example, that having Menya wash down her meds with a berry smoothie might make the medication more palatable. Menya downed the smoothie and the meds—and then gagged. The smoothie and medication exploded out of her mouth, covering a wide swath including herself, Randi and the bed.

Nights were becoming difficult because Menya was sleeping more during the day and then was up at night. I

suggested to Pete that I might stay over in case there was
something I could do to help. I would sleep on the couch
in the living room downstairs. The first night I spent there,
I heard a loud thump and then Pete calling me. It was
3 a.m. He'd been trying to transfer Menya from their bed
to the wheelchair to take her to the bathroom. They'd fall-
en and had become entangled in one another's legs. Menya
had been Rubenesque since her teens. The Decadron, her
appetite for sweets, and her now sedentary existence, had
made her bloated and much heavier. I helped Pete up, the
two of us got Menya into her wheelchair, and I slipped
back downstairs. The following night, I'd just settled in
around midnight when Pete came down to say—sheep-
ishly—that Menya didn't want me (or anyone) staying
over. She wanted to be alone in the house with him. I
gritted my teeth and left, wondering how long Pete could
carry on by himself.

The next few days were especially difficult. Menya began vomiting and it took two days to trace the cause back
to a morphine patch intended to ease her pain. She was
put on Haldol, an antipsychotic drug that also relieves
nausea. It worked. But the fact that she was losing more
and more control made her obsessive about the things
she could control. Everything in the room had to be in

exactly the right place. If we understood what she wanted, we were, of course, happy to oblige. But she was now frequently saying the opposite of what she meant. And she kept telling Pete how badly he was looking after her. "It hurts like hell," he wrote on October 3, "but I'm getting better at taking it for what it is—frustration."

There was now a new development. Menya was going blind, and it was happening quickly. On Friday, October 6, as Randi was leaving for the weekend, Menya gave her a list of things to pick up for Monday, then added impishly, "Oh, by the way, would you come dressed as a clown on Monday?" Randi did. She came as Njala, the wife of Njal, the hero of Menya's favourite Icelandic saga. Njal is wise, but sadly realizes that wisdom can't save him from death. Randi as Njala, turned out to be one of the last things Menya actually saw. "She's pretty much blind now," Pete wrote on Thursday October 12.

The blindness increased her frustration. She was now getting up at 3 a.m. and staying awake the rest of the night. Some nights Pete would take her to the hospital bed in the back room and try to get back to sleep himself. "Last night she didn't want to go there," he wrote, "so I stayed up with her.... We talked about suicide. Menya doesn't see the point in going on. There are nice moments but the background is pain and frustration. So much for dying with dignity...."

Menya finally agreed to talk to June Galbraith about additional services available through Trinity Home Hospice (THH). After their October 7 meeting, Menya agreed to allow Janet, a harpist friend of June's, to visit on a regular basis to play for her. (Janet has since become part of a Healing Minstrels Program that THH has made available to its clients.) Menya also agreed to allow one THH volunteer, Nancy, to visit her on Saturday mornings. Nancy paid her first visit on October 14 and the two of them hit it off. Menya had also begun allowing a friend, Roben, to stay over on Friday nights. The changes in the schedule meant that Pete could have a Friday night and Saturday morning to himself to sleep, exercise, shop or whatever. Meanwhile, friends continued to send in gourmet meals and other groceries; the fridge was always overflowing. Menya was still enjoying food.

Her condition stabilized for the next ten days. But on October 23, the situation worsened again. She insisted on going downstairs on the stair lift but was too weak. She lay in bed howling. A VON nurse tried to change the catheter but the attempt hurt too much. "This morning," Pete wrote, "she *meant* to say that she wanted to use the commode...but what she *actually* said was that she wanted to go downstairs. It took us a while to figure it out.... Last week Menya said if she were a dog, they'd be able to put her out of her misery."

By October 30, Menya was a lot worse. "The end is very near," Pete wrote. "She has been blind for two weeks, has no use of her right side, and finds it hard to find words. Menya recently decided to go on a pain pump, which will give her a strong dose of the narcotic Dilaudid to control pain and keep her sedated. There are two bits of good news in all this: First, the end to Menya's suffering is in sight. When they hook her up to the pump tonight, it'll take about twenty-four hours to get to the sleepy state; from then on she'll be mostly out of it. The other good news is that when Menya dies, it will be peaceful and pain-free, and she'll be surrounded by people who love her."

"Shit, shit, shit," replied one of their many e-mail correspondents.

But the pain pump didn't work; intravenous Dilaudid made Menya nauseated. It was back to the drawing board.

CHAPTER THREE

November 2000

TRINITY HOME HOSPICE grew out of an informal
initiative. In the mid-1980s, a group of women
and men from the congregation of the Church of the
Holy Trinity in downtown Toronto rallied around a
friend, Margaret Frazer, a single woman with no family,
who had terminal cancer and wanted to die at home. June
Callwood, one of her caregivers, documented the experience in *Twelve Weeks in Spring*. The book served as inspi-
ration and model for those who created Trinity Home
Hospice in 1988. THH is an independent, non-denomina-
tional and non-profit organization, made up of seven staff
people and 120 volunteers, eighty of whom have had at
least thirty hours of training. The others are board mem-

bers, committee members, special events help, etc.

Pete now invited Trinity Home Hospice to become fully involved in Menya's care. Menya agreed—reluctantly. THH would set up a 24/7 schedule; the caregiving team would be made up of friends, family and trained THH volunteers, each of whom would commit to one four-hour shift a week. Representatives of the three agencies that would be involved in Menya's care met at the house on November 8. The Hospice Palliative Care Network (HPCNET) would provide round-the-clock access to a doctor and a nurse. Through HPCNET, a psycho-social worker would be available to the team. The Community Care Access Centre (CCAC) would provide homemakers, medical supplies and equipment. Through CCAC a VON nurse would continue to visit daily, more often when needed. In addition to the volunteers, THH would also schedule complementary therapists—the harpist, a reflexologist, as well as Reiki and practitioners of therapeutic touch.

Following the November 8 meeting, I sent an e-mail to immediate family members who lived out-of-town—Mary Bevin (Pete's mother in England) and Jen and Ben (Menya's brother and sister). "The reason we met," I wrote, "is that as weeks stretch into months, the burden on Pete grows…. Because she can't see his face, she reads his tired voice as meaning, 'He doesn't love me any more.' THH is setting up a schedule involving friends, family and trained volunteers. Everyone actively involved in Menya's care will meet on November 14."

At that meeting, June Galbraith emphasized that Menya was in charge of her care team. It was her life, her journey and her death. Her illness had taken many of her choices away, but there were still things she could control; our job was to be there for her. Menya had already made it clear that she wanted to be moved downstairs, to be part of everything that was going on. We would do this as soon as possible. Except for Pete, Menya didn't want men involved in her intimate care, though we could help in other ways. Although her hopes had diminished, June said, there were still things she could hope for. To be free of pain. To have time to say good-bye to everyone she wanted to. To finish unfinished business.

As caregivers, we would keep two sets of records. Medical details—when medication was taken, the dosage, whether she'd had bowel movements, and so on—would continue to be recorded in a log with a green cover. (The Green Book, as we called it, had been kept since early October.) A Blue Book would serve as an anecdotal record, written by the caregivers to keep other caregivers informed, and as a permanent record for the family. The Blue Book also contained several pages of information to remind caregivers about physical aspects of caregiving—mouth and skin care, infection control, transfers, etc.

Pete would cover four nights a week, Roben would do Friday nights, and professional caregivers the other two. Randi would continue to work four mornings a week. Homemakers would come in every day from 11 a.m. to 2 p.m., seven days a week. They would be relieved at 2 p.m. by a volunteer caregiver. Another volunteer would take over at 6. The overnight shift would begin at 10.

Because they lived so far away, it was difficult to schedule members of Menya and Pete's immediate families. Menya's sister Jen, her husband and two children, lived in western Michigan; her brother Ben, his wife and three children, lived in Ottawa. They visited as often as they could, usually one long weekend every two or three weeks. When they were in Toronto, they could be part of the team as extras and were thus able to maintain their role as family, the role Pete was trying to get back. Menya's mother, Carla, lives in Toronto and was a frequent visitor. But because she has emphysema, physical caregiving was out of the question. Pete has no siblings and no family other than his widowed mother in England, who visited on several occasions. I was on sabbatical and writing a book; my time was flexible and Joy, my partner, was more than accommodating, as were the partners of so many of the caregivers.

2

FROM THIS POINT ON, Menya's story is largely told through entries in the Blue Book. For ease of telling, I've compressed the entries. Readers should remember that far more people were involved in Menya's care than the number of voices below might suggest, and not everyone felt comfortable writing in the Blue Book. Occasionally, as indicated by [square brackets], I've added some explanatory or bridging comments. I've placed an asterisk after the names of THH volunteers. The first entry in the Blue Book turned out to be mine.

Saturday November 18, afternoon, Morris
Brought some fruit and peameal bacon sandwiches from the St. Lawrence Market at around 1 p.m. [Joy and I made

that a weekly habit.] Menya was calm at first but when the subject turned to her move downstairs, she became agitated about the number of beds and floor-to-ceiling poles and their location. Her talk was both confused—and confusing. She and Pete became more and more frustrated; they eventually phoned Randi to see what her understanding was. At that point, I went downstairs to be out of the way. When I went back up, Menya was in tears and Pete was looking extremely discouraged. The only thing that was clear to me was that Menya wanted to be in the same bed as Pete as much of the time as possible.

Sunday November 19, morning, Nancy*
Menya seemed much less vigorous than she was last Sunday, rather worn out (as was Pete). I played some music and massaged her feet and legs and she slept for most of the morning. When she woke up, we had a wee chat. Menya is quite depressed and, as she put it, 'feeling unloved.' I asked her to give the care team a chance to 'care' for her in all senses of the word.

Monday November 20, morning, Randi
Pete is toast, crispy, burnt out, sleep-deprived, can't see it through, ready to check out, or check into a hotel. Menya

woke him to tell him there was something wrong, but she couldn't communicate it. She was so exasperated that she began screaming at him. I feel tired and drained too. Menya said she'd felt 'patronized' by me [during the Saturday phone discussion about the downstairs arrangements]. I apologized. She's especially sensitive to not being heard because she has such a hard time expressing herself. Pete and I had to admit that we don't know how we'll manage the move downstairs. It will take careful planning.

Because Menya had a terrible burning sensation, the VON nurse removed the catheter; it will be replaced tomorrow (hopefully). In the meantime it's diapers.... Faye [the homemaker], Ann [a volunteer] and I got Menya into the bath. It was worth the effort just to see her relief and pleasure. We sang a few songs at the top of our lungs ('Drunken sailor', and 'Today while the blossoms')— Menya on harmonies.

As I write, Ann and Menya are giggling as they reminisce. Nice to hear.

Monday November 20, afternoon, Ann
Over lunch Menya talked about how easily words come for 'frivolous topics' but how much more difficult it is to speak about emotionally charged subjects. She says

there's a fine line between caregivers 'helping her out' if she's struggling and their trying to finish her sentences for her.

Monday November 20, evening, Roben
Menya didn't seem to recognize my voice at first, so I swore. 'Roben,' sez she. We continued to exchange profanities and strange stories…. Menya expressed disdain at the possibility of living long enough to have to write Christmas cards. We laughed.

Tuesday November 21, morning, Randi
She's had a pretty good morning, relatively pain and nausea free. As I fed her dry corn flakes and cut strawberries (her request), I kept losing flakes on her front. Menya suggested that were I to look for a similar job in the future, I shouldn't put 'feeding' on my résumé. Oh well.

She frequently can't find the right words, the result being embarrassment and frustration both on her part (and the caregiver's). It helps to zero in on physical needs: Does she want to sit on the commode? Does she want the bed adjusted? Does she want medication? Name the choices. Be patient and calm; keep your sense of humour. Encourage Menya to take her time.

Tuesday November 21, evening, Morris
Training session for non-THH members of the team
The meeting was long and stressful. When the team arrived, Pete and Menya were at an impasse—she wanted something and was exasperated that he couldn't understand what it was. Pete was in tears. After a while, team members went upstairs for a demonstration of how to transfer Menya to the commode and off, and from one bed to the other. She enjoyed the attention. After everyone was back downstairs, Janet, an old family friend, commented on how difficult the situation is. On the one hand, the team is there to take care of Menya's needs, but she still wants and expects Pete to do that. It wasn't going to be an easy transition. Pete, she said, has gone from being a mutual partner to being the father of a difficult child.

Thursday November 23, afternoon, Jennifer M.
Right leg uncomfortable; took time and medication to get it right. Listened to a beautiful CD of Menya singing and playing the harp.

[Ten years earlier, Menya had done a rough taping of herself singing and playing for a friend who was dying of cancer. The tapes, which Menya had forgotten, had come full circle. Roben's husband, Ross, a sound engineer, had cleaned them up and transferred them to CDs. Menya was delighting in sharing the music with her caregivers.]

Thursday November 24, overnight, Jen W. [Menya's sister]
A lovely evening. Menya is only in slight discomfort. No tears and very little frustration. She was having trouble enunciating and finding words, but she paused and resumed her thoughts with some success. She drifted to sleep to the sound of her own music around 11:30 p.m. She spent ten minutes groping around the bed before she slept. She removed all the pillows and blankets and tried to put them on the cluttered bedside table. Then she kept feeling around for the missing head pillow; grasping the pole and bed controls; feeling around on the table to see what was where; while moving her left leg from floor to bed, back and forth. I don't think she was looking for anything in particular, just fixing its position in her mind.

Friday November 24, overnight, Roben
We listened to the CDs Ross made for Menya…. I am overwhelmed by her gratitude…. I knew that copies of the music would be a great thing for friends and family in the future but Menya is able to relive a happier time now. Yay! Words came slowly but we tried to be patient with one

another. She spoke briefly on the phone with Jen and with an old high school friend. Fell into a contented sleep with Theo at 11 p.m.

[Theo was one of Menya and Pete's three cats. They'd acquired two in England, Theo and Rasputin, and brought them to Canada. Subsequently, they adopted a third cat, a stray they named Dante. Menya, who loved cats, was especially attached to Theo.]

Saturday, November 25, afternoon
[Pete and some friends moved Menya downstairs. The king-size bed was moved from their bedroom and now stood by the living room window. The hospital bed was shifted from the guest room to the middle of the living/dining room. A table was covered with medical supplies, which overflowed onto the floor. The dining room table was covered with various kinds of chocolate.]

Sunday November 26, morning, Nancy*
This is Menya's first full day downstairs. The von nurse was here when I arrived…. We helped Menya to sit up so she could drink some hot chocolate. Took a while to get her settled again…. Menya kept insisting on a bath, although she was in the midst of having one, albeit a sponge

bath. She was increasingly frustrated, then agitated, and finally just royally pissed off. I asked Pete to mediate.... It seems she wanted something to eat, not a bath.... I gave Menya a foot massage, with lullaby music in the background; she relaxed considerably and then insisted on giving me a back massage. How could I refuse?

[Caregivers' use of phrases such as 'Menya asked' or 'Menya said' had by now become shorthand for a complicated process that involved asking questions and trying to decipher answers, all the while remembering that what Menya literally said wasn't necessarily what she meant.]

Monday November 27, morning, Randi

When I arrived this morning, Menya was sitting on the floor, with Dolores the overnight homemaker and Pete trying to lift her back into bed. Finally the three of us managed...she lay there flopped at a right angle to recover. She had landed on the floor en route to the commode. Menya asked that her pills be within reach so she could take them herself.... I balked, concerned that she might be confused about what she was taking and when she'd last taken it. [As well, Menya had been talking suicide.]

I felt crabby earlier because I'm already feeling back discomfort as a result of dealing with the king-size bed. I won't be able to hold out physically without the aid of the adjustable hospital bed for transfers.

Tuesday November 28, afternoon, Morris
Thinking back on it, I had my last real conversation with Menya—one that went back and forth and didn't involve a lot of confusion and guesswork—on November 17. We held hands and talked about mutual friends; about her nieces and nephews; about our respective attitudes toward death. Eleven days later, that kind of talk is no longer possible.

[Although Menya had lost her sight, her hearing remained keen. At one point she heard a woman talking flirtatiously to Pete in the kitchen. "I'm not dead yet!" she called out in a bemused voice. It was one of the last clear sentences she spoke.]

Tuesday November 28, afternoon, Linda*
I gave her lunch, delicious smoked salmon and bagels. She sat up in bed while I brushed her hair and wiped her face with a washcloth. I put some lipstick and blush on her.

[Menya had loved dressing up since she was a child. Wearing jewellery and dressed in robes, her long hair flowing, she loved making dramatic entrances at SCA and other events. She specialized in the role of queen.]

Tuesday November 28, e-mail from Ben to Pete
I know your relationship [with Menya] has been extraordinarily challenging and draining.... The only parallel I have is fatherhood. From that I know that even when things are going wonderfully and the rewards are great, the energy, patience and sacrifice required each day don't come without a constant effort of will. (And believe me, there have been plenty of days when I haven't measured up.).... I was touched by the chapter you gave me to read on Sunday [from *Before I Say Goodbye*, by Ruth Picardie] and especially by the part in which Matt faces the fact that his relationship has become 'one way'—that he's probably received as much love from his wife as he is going to get... while the effort required to care for her is increasing.... I doubt you get direct thanks from Menya nearly as often as you deserve, or feel her there, with and for you, in the way that made you want to marry her in the first place.

Wednesday November 29, evening, Pete
Theo died about two hours ago, hit by a car. Back in England, when we first brought him home, Menya felt guilty—we had decided to get two cats—but she didn't feel she could ever love another as much as she loved Theo. He was dog-like: loyal, loved to play fetch, always follow-

ing people around. It took him awhile but he eventually learned how to catch birds and mice. One time he brought a half-dead bird in to show Menya during a Reiki treatment. Not appreciated. He loved shrimp tails. We tried giving him a whole shrimp once, but he couldn't figure out what the fleshy bit was for.

Thursday November 30, morning, Randi
I was saddened to hear about Theo when I arrived. I had a good cry on Menya's shoulder.... through many tears she expressed how angry and sad she felt that she didn't get to say goodbye. She couldn't bear the thought of him just being carted off in a cardboard box. She expressed feelings of abandonment, adding that she felt abandoned by me (all this through a fog). I think the changes—a new care team, the move downstairs—have been very hard on her. I asked if she identified with Theo. 'Yes!' she said. This has been an opportunity...to express her grief, fear and frustration about her own death. I put on a CD of Mozart's *Requiem*.

Thursday November 30, afternoon, Jennifer M.
We chatted about various things and told silly jokes. Good to see Menya laugh. Pete moved Menya to the king-size bed. After he went upstairs, we talked quietly while I mas-

saged her feet. She had several moments of distress about her inability to make herself understood—the wrong words kept coming out. I lay in bed beside her while she cried. I couldn't understand much but it was about waiting to die and not understanding why she was still here. Expressing her frustration made her feel better.... I fed her some date square and read a few chapters of Harry Potter, which she enjoyed.

[Menya had announced at one point that she wasn't going to read any of the Harry Potter books until she could read all seven of them. It was one way of telling herself—and us—that she was going to be around at least until then. Now she was eager to hear as much Harry Potter as she could.]

CHAPTER FOUR
December 2000

Friday December 1, afternoon, Ben

Menya had a craving for chicken, so I cooked some up with mushroom sauce. She seems concerned with my comfort and seeing that I have enough of everything. She said that perhaps we were all getting tired of her. I said on the contrary, that I wished I could do more, and that she shouldn't worry about us. One of the complementary caregivers gave Menya a massage, after which she slept until 5:15 p.m.

Friday December 1, overnight, Roben

So sad about Theo.... I think the karma fairy got the wrong bloody house. Menya has just pulled the sheets up over her head in her sleep and the effect is disconcerting.

Passed some time dusting her harps. [Menya had collected a number of old instruments, including a second harp.] She talked for a while, slowly and deliberately, not just about Theo's loss but the accumulated losses: the ability to see, to play music, to get around, to be independent. She'd lost her breast, her hair—and now her cat. Theo was the last straw.

Sunday December 3, morning, Nancy*
A bright, brilliant, sunny morning—but cold!—Menya wanted to hear all about what it was like outside. She misses the world. Seeing it. Being a part of it. We had about an hour together to talk—our quiet time before the nurse came. Menya talked about 'too many losses, too much sorrow' and that she 'couldn't take it any more.' She talked about there no longer being 'hope'.… After the nurse and I helped her to lie down in the hospital bed, she decided she wanted to 'see' the world. We moved her to the king-size bed, drew back the drapes and described the world, right down to the woman with the shocking turquoise hair across the street.

Tuesday December 5, late afternoon, Pete
Menya has been very confused the last couple of days. She isn't sure where she is or what is going on. She often needs

reassurance that we aren't lying to her. Last night we had a hard time giving her medication, and then she refused to let us disconnect the IV—we had to hold her down to take it off. She doesn't remember that.

Tuesday December 5, evening, Morris
Team meeting
June Galbraith distributed the schedule for the next two weeks. We talked about Menya's confusion and that her mistrust was verging on paranoia. The supervising nurse thought this phase would pass; she said that as Menya's condition deteriorates, there will be less brain function and that her mind will slow. Because she'll be less and less able to express pain verbally, it becomes increasingly important for us to watch for other signs, such as facial expressions and restlessness.

June asked us about our Christmas plans. She said that through a partnership with the Royal York Hotel, THH could offer free accommodation at the hotel to members of Menya and Pete's families over Christmas and New Year's. That would make it easier for Jen and Ben, their partners, and Menya's five nieces and nephews to visit at the same time. On other occasions Jen and Ben had been coming in on their own.

I found myself thrown by June's question. I'd assumed that Menya would be dead by Christmas. I hadn't expected her to live much beyond the end of October. The truth was I wanted it to be over. Then, like the character in Beckett who says, 'I can't go on, I'll go on,' I psyched myself up for whatever came next. I don't know how many others shared this feeling. It's not something we talked about. It also dawned on me that we had to revise our funeral plans. Like many rural cemeteries, the cemetery in Castleton doesn't dig graves in the winter. People who die then have to be stored in a vault to await spring burial.

Thursday December 7, afternoon, Jennifer M.
Menya had a difficult afternoon…. She was in good spirits when I arrived but became quite disoriented, getting up and down. Quite difficult to understand her. Carla visited. Then Dr. John and his wife, Grace, came. Menya is worried about 'being too much trouble.'

Friday December 8, morning, Randi
Menya sad at first—telling us she wants to trust us but it's hard. As the morning progressed, she was calm, quiet, even chuckling and laughing at times. We had a new VON

nurse who required a bit of instruction from the old pro, Pete. (He donned his nurse's cap again—quite fetching.)

*Sunday December 10, morning, Nancy**
I arrived bright and early to two sleeping beauties. The VON nurse gave Menya a scrub and she sat up for a while in the chair. I gave her some waffles for breakfast (yum!) This is my first visit in which Menya and I haven't talked the whole time. She gets so frustrated trying to speak and make herself understood.... I told her how truly and well-loved she is. She said she doesn't feel loveable.

Monday December 11, morning, Randi
Menya was relatively peaceful this morning. Had already transferred from the king-size bed to the hospital bed by the time I arrived.... I read her the last chapter of *The House at Pooh Corner*, which ends: "wherever they go, and whatever happens to them on the way, in that enchanted place on the top of the Forest, a little boy and his Bear will always be playing." Menya listened contentedly, know-ingly, especially identifying with Eeyore, who was being left behind. Then we sang songs together, me mostly, with Menya chiming in a note here and there: 'Gloucester was-

sail,' 'Morning Morgantown,' 'The parting glass,' and 'She moved through the fair.'

Monday December 11, June Galbraith
E-mail to care team
During the past weekend, sad and significant changes have been noted in Menya's condition.... Pete asked that the team be informed, so that you'll be aware of these changes before you visit. Menya is sleeping peacefully now most of the time.... When awake she is confused and her consciousness level is lower. She is eating very little and taking only small amounts of fluids. The colour of her urine is dark and reduced in quantity. She has requested that her...Decadron be reduced by half. Menya is still asking to transfer to the commode, but may not be able to do so much longer.

Tuesday December 12, evening, Roben
Communication is more difficult. This creates a problem with most transfers. She says left, she means right; she wants to lie down, she stands...poor pet. I got rather forceful in my last transfer—she'd fallen twice yesterday. I asked her to trust me and let me lead. Once she was lying down again, I asked if she believed that I loved her. She said, 'yes,'

and smiled. I assured her that if and when the day comes that she stopped believing me, I would still love her.

Wednesday December 13, morning, Sue M.*

Arrived to find the dangerous duo getting up for the day. Menya transferred from the king-size bed to the hospital bed via the commode. The VON nurse and homemaker arrived. By asking a series of 'yes/no' questions, we were able to get her needs met. Menya seems more at peace than last Wednesday. Her 'monthly friend' arrived today.

[Menya's menstrual periods had continued despite chemo and radiation. Early on I'd given her a copy of *Tuesdays With Morrie*. Like Morrie, she had slowly and painfully come to accept that her dignity wasn't ultimately vested in who wiped her ass or changed her pads.]

Thursday December 14, morning, Randi

As I write, Menya is contentedly eating her dessert after a hot shepherd's pie for lunch. Her appetite has been good. The nurse removed the tensor from her right ankle, strained when she fell during a transfer, and rubbed in some Arnica gel. This is day two (three?) of her period. The pads go on easiest from back to front, quickly, while Menya is standing. She was last changed around noon.

Friday December 15, afternoon, Jen W.
Menya restless and trying to stand up, without a clear idea of where she wanted to go. Sue B. [the regular Friday afternoon volunteer] and I got her onto the chair and spent considerable time trying to understand where she wanted to be. There was a good deal of stony silence; Menya kept fumbling for the pole, as if she were about to stand. She eventually agreed that she wanted to be in the king-size bed but that transfer wasn't successful. After long and patient listening and utter failure to understand, we decided that she really ought to be in the hospital bed, so that's what we did. I'm worried about her need to get up and down without warning (at one point she stood and sat probably ten times in a row). *Please* don't leave her alone if she seems fidgety; try to figure out if she has a reason before she gets up.

Friday December 15, overnight, Roben
Pete came by to say he was going out for dinner with Jen and Morris and was that okay. Menya pointed to the door and told him to get out, showing us she was still able to joke. Unfortunately, as the discussion progressed, we misunderstood something she said to mean that she really wanted Pete to stay. When she realized what we thought

she meant, she covered her face with the comforter and cried. Later with Johanna and Jen and Pete, we had another awkward moment. The subject of Menya's intimate care came up. She became uncomfortable and told Pete to shut up. All of us had been part of the conversation but she saw Pete as the instigator. She shouted him down every time he spoke. I apologized for my part in the discussion, saying that issues of private and public were fuzzy to me.*

In some ways I feel that what I do around here is pretty damn ham-handed and inadequate. However, there's a part of me that feels that by doing good things for good people, we become instruments of positive karma. Bullshit

---

* Part of treating patients with dignity is not talking about them in their presence. Some years before Menya became ill, I wrote a long article about a dear friend, whose death, like hers, had been hard. My friend had asked me to tell her story honestly, messy bits and all. When Menya asked me if I would write something about her, she specifically referred to this article about my friend Elizabeth as the model she had in mind. In writing and editing this piece, I've taken my cue from that conversation. It's true that Menya didn't like hearing people joking or talking about her intimate care in her presence. Few of us would. But like my friend, she felt differently about her story being told truthfully after she was gone.

bits of me have been burned away in recent months and I am more myself—the enduring part.

Saturday December 16, afternoon, Pete
Roben says above that she feels that what she does here is inadequate. I've heard that from others. Here's what I think and I hope it helps: There are a lot of people who die suddenly in hospital, without being able to say goodbye. There are a lot of people who get sent off to nursing homes, where they won't bother their families. There are a lot of people whose friends abandon them when the going gets tough. All of these people would give anything to die like Menya—loved, at home, cared for and surrounded by good people. That's the gift that you're giving. I thank you all.

Saturday December 16, afternoon and overnight, Jen W.
Menya slept all morning and took ages to come round. At first she was grouchy and slapping people's hands away. Transfers were painful and she refused help with smoothing bedclothes, etc. and asked us to go away.... Got out one vehement sentence: 'I don't know!' in the midst of us asking questions to see what she wanted. Refused any and all food and drink until Fiona [an old friend] arrived with chocolate gingers. Her visit was just the thing—cheerful

chat and anecdotes. Menya was following and participated with laughs, groans, etc. This set the tone for a very nice evening—she was relaxed and alert enough to participate co-operatively in transfers and decisions. It's such a *relief* not to be battling her for every leg shift and pillow fluff.... There was less of the compulsive up-and-downs. No BMs today or yesterday. Period is almost over. She wanted to ride her stair lift up and down just for fun, but we nixed that for lack of manpower and settled instead for fresh air at the front door. Read lots of Harry Potter.

Sunday December 17, morning, Nancy*
I arrived and Jen had everything in hand. I had an amazing dream last night. I arrived for my shift, went over to Menya's bed and saw that she was there—as a little girl. And she was happy and laughing. She reached up and touched my face and said, 'I know who you are!' Then she crawled into my lap; I wrapped my arms around her, and we rocked together.

I gave Menya a foot massage which seemed to relax her. Then we listened to some smoky jazz by Keith Jarrett. All in all Menya seems pretty quiet. Jen and Pete and I had tears together.... I won't be back for two weeks, I'm sorry to say. But I will be carrying Menya in my heart.

Sunday December 17, evening, Sheri
Menya was restless this evening. She tried to leave the bed by herself. When I offered assistance, she seemed startled, as if she hadn't realized what she was doing. She fluctuated between being too hot and too cold and between periods of confusion and lucidity. At one point she kicked off her blankets and objected to having them anywhere near her.

Tuesday December 19, morning, Randi
Menya attempted for quite a while to say something. This frustrated her to tears. I finally asked if she was tired of all this, to which she answered a very clear, 'Yes!', and cried. The air mattress for her bed arrived today. New gadgets to adjust to. Menya had a bemused smile as the bed was deflated and inflated and as she tried various positions. [The experiment lasted for only a few days—the mattress wasn't safe; she was rolling off.]

Tuesday December 19, evening, Morris
Team meeting
We reviewed the schedule. Some shifts during the holiday season will be covered by additional THH volunteers to give regular caregivers more time with their families. Homemaking hours have been increased to five and a

half hours—8:30 a.m. to 2 p.m. Members of the team expressed considerable sadness and frustration about the trouble they have understanding Menya and, as a result, not being able to do what she wants or needs. The supervising nurse, Debbie, said that communication would likely become even more difficult. Although it's hard, we have to accept that we won't always understand Menya. She herself may become more accepting of that.

Although transfers to the commode continue, Menya needs far more assistance. When the time comes for her to be toileted in bed, we'll have a training session for those who haven't had one. Menya has decided to cut her use of Decadron in half and may discontinue it entirely. It was clear that her quality of life was better off decadron. But she'll have to take more Dilantin because without decadron, the number of seizures will increase. If Menya refuses her meds, we were told, that's okay, but we need to make sure that's recorded in the Green Book. Pete mentioned that Menya is occasionally upset by visitors who stay too long or attempt 'deep' conversations. We agreed that caregivers should step in if it seems appropriate. Offer the visitor tea or coffee; invite them to read the Blue Book. Apart from family and close friends, most visits should be limited to fifteen minutes.

Thursday December 21, morning, Randi

Menya hasn't eaten anything and has taken only a few sips of water. At first it was 'no' to everything: food, music, story. She did, however, agree to her pain meds and to a manicure. I soaked her hand in warm soapy water, massaged her arm, shoulder and hand, cleaned her nails and applied fresh nail polish. She smiled and chuckled a few times as I reminded her of some of the funny things she's said since I began caring for her, "Am I just being negative, or does this suck?" "Do you think I should get my teeth straightened?" Sometimes she'd ask me to tell her a story. But it had to be good. Once when I was trying to tell one, she interrupted, and asked, "Is this story going anywhere?"

Faye and the VON nurse managed to do some minimal body washing and pericare, including the application of cream to the rash in her stomach folds. Menya remained lying down for this. She's dozing now while Faye and I decorate a bit for Christmas.

Thursday, December 21, afternoon, Jennifer M.

Menya seems the most peaceful I have seen her yet. She was awake and clearly 'with it' all afternoon, though quiet. I massaged her feet and hands. We chatted about many things—she smiled, nodded, grimaced or grunted at appropriate points. Her 'requests'—move this, get water, stop reading, etc.—were all easy to understand because she clearly said 'Yes' or 'No' to everything I asked. At one point I said that by letting us care for her, she was giving to us. She nodded and stroked my hand…. Dr. John arrived about 5:30 while we were listening to some quiet music.

Thursday December 21, evening, Roben
Arrived to a house of mirth, around 6 p.m. Dr. John, Menya, Janet and I chatted happily about ethics, religion, faith and the fate of mankind. Although Menya's conversational involvement was limited to facial expressions and 'yes'es and 'no's, it felt as though she was taking as active a part as the rest of us. Because it was solstice, I had brought books for Janet and Dr. John, and a potato whistle for Menya. I refused to tell her what it was until she'd turned it over a few times and tried to guess. She seemed to enjoy the game. I remarked that for the darkest night of the year, we were having a pretty good time. Janet taught me a solstice chant. Dr. John left before the VON arrived.

Thursday December 21, evening, Janet
Brian, the VON nurse, arrived shortly after 8 p.m.—cheerful and friendly. He tried three times to flush out the porta-

cath but it was clogged. [A portacath is a device surgically implanted in a patient who requires frequent intravenous medication.] Brian phoned an IV specialist, whose advice was that we take Menya to the hospital where the porta-cath was implanted. They would know what to do. Menya tried and tried to talk. Couldn't, of course. We tried to suggest what she might be thinking: that she has made a clear decision against further treatment; that she isn't try-ing to prolong her life; that she's had enough hospital trips. But we couldn't be sure. Brian tried to reach Pete by cell phone but couldn't. Menya wept. A lot. Pete was home at 9:30. Menya made it clear—*no* hospital.

Friday December 22, morning, Randi
Pete filled Faye [the homemaker] and me in on last night's event. VON nurse arrived and we all conferred. Menya will take her meds—Dilantin and Decadron—orally for as long as possible. The transfer to the hospital bed went smoothly—there were two of us helping—me keeping a close watch on her trick leg and foot....

She was eager to eat some *Krumkaker* with whipped cream and lingonberries [a Norwegian Christmas treat] and liked it a lot. I read some Harry Potter as she snug-gled under the butterfly quilt her maternal grandmother made for her. She was attentive and responsive, 'oooing' at all the scary bits.

Friday December 22, June Galbraith
E-mail to care team
Menya's portacath blocked on the evening of December 21 and is now non-functioning.... The IV is therefore discontinued. All meds will be taken orally. When Menya is no longer able to swallow them, a decision will be made about how to proceed. She needs to be sitting up for all fluid and food intake, to prevent choking. Menya is sleeping more and appears to be less agitated. She is still transferring to the commode, but two people are really needed for the transfer. If Menya wants to remain on the commode for a period of time, keep her warm and stay close. Menya still prefers to be in the king-size bed at times.

Friday December 22, evening and overnight, Roben
Lots of talk, frustration and tears. Menya wanted to talk about the fact that she's scared of dying.... She managed some words, slowly and painstakingly: 'I don't want to keep...if there's no reason' and 'I don't know what to do.' Menya wouldn't talk while Pete was in the room. Clammed up tight during dinner. I remembered Janet's obser-

vation last night that Menya might be projecting anger at Pete because he was out during the portacath disaster. When he left the room I asked her what was up, was she mad at him? She said no.

Saturday December 23, morning, Sheri
Menya slept peacefully all morning. Pete was feeling overwhelmed. Roben spent time with him, helping him delegate some things.

Saturday December 23, evening, Roben
Pete and I were alone with Menya. I told her I wanted to say a few words about something I was about to give her. I talked about how much I'd learned as a result of being part of her care team. She'd taught me more about life and death and spiritual transformation than anyone. I wanted her to know how much I valued her as a friend and teacher. I reached under my shirt and pulled out a strand of amber, looping it onto her hand. (Menya and I had met in the Wiccan community, where amber is an important symbol of initiation.) I told her that I'd been given this strand at my initiation and I wanted her to have it. My only stipulation was that she not pass it on to anyone else. If she wished, we could bury it with her, or

if she preferred, I would toss it into the sea in her name. She chose the latter.

Sunday December 24, morning, Randi

Menya was sitting and standing in her restless way when I arrived. We did the 'many questions' routine to which every response was 'No.' She smiled at times, relishing how contrary she was being, but eventually said 'Yes' to french toast with berries.

She refused medication of any kind all morning. I worry that this will make the pain worse when it hits. But there's no forcing her. She finally agreed to a minimal wash, including pericare. She also said 'Yes', with a smile, to a foot massage.

Christmas, afternoon, Morris

Menya and Pete had Christmas morning to themselves. I arrived just after noon. Put turkey, prepared by a neighbour, in the oven, and then read Harry Potter to Menya. A substitute THH volunteer arrived, followed by friends. Menya seemed engaged in the conversation. Christmas dinner at 5 p.m. Menya ate a little and took a few sips of fluid. After she fell asleep, I sat quietly by her bed for a while and headed home.

*Tuesday December 26, morning, Sue M.**

Arrived to find Menya and Pete sleeping soundly. Menya very restless this morning, refusing everything but a couple of sips of water. Put a new catheter drainage bag on at 1 p.m. (only 600 cc for past 48 hours.) Has our Menya made a decision to stop eating and drinking?

Tuesday December 26, evening, Roben

Menya is sleeping with most of her face under the blanket. (I hate it when she does that. Sometimes she does it because she knows I hate it.) Soon she awoke and had three noodles, two bits of sundried tomato, one slice of mushroom, and three segments of clementine—Weight Watchers would be proud. As soon as she heard her nieces' and nephews' voices, her whole body tensed with excitement and her face lit up with the biggest Menya smile I'd seen in weeks. She listened appreciatively to various conversations and anecdotes and remained alert and cheerful, no mean feat for her these days. I tried to fade into the background but I was soon inducted into a secret archaeological spy club by Graeme, 5, and Hannah, 4. (Noah, 12, Emma, 9, and Paul, 3, were otherwise occupied, Paul under an upside down basket chair.) Family members took turns holding Menya's hand and stroking her hair. Near the end of the visit they lit Hanukkah candles. Menya seemed to particularly enjoy the family singing together; her mouth formed some of the words. After everyone left there were tears.

Thursday December 28, morning, Randi
Menya was relatively aware this morning. She enjoyed my reading Harry Potter as she lay on her side. She had a brief crying spell. She's afraid—of dying and of pain. I reassured her that we are going to keep her as safe and comfortable as possible. Faye gave her a wash, including hair, and soon after she had a visit from some old friends. She was pleased to see them, but after half an hour, she was tired.

Thursday December 28, 8 p.m., Roben
Kate was here from 6 to 10 p.m. Apparently Menya had a seizure between 6 and 8 p.m., which as usual, tired and confused her. She seemed upset when I arrived, not wishing to be touched or spoken to, no music, just left alone, please. We (Pete, Kate, Ben and I) sat in the kitchen. After a while, Menya let Kate sit with her and gradually we all joined in. I told embarrassing stories about my courtship with Ross. Menya seemed to appreciate hearing of this

folly; she also seemed tired. I know she finds the seizures upsetting. We're all pretty edgy this evening.

Friday December 29, afternoon, Jen W.
Sue B., Menya and I sat around and talked merrily about all sorts of romantic, medical, festive and other occasions. Menya joined in with facial expressions and laughter. Dr. John and Grace arrived. We left Grace with Menya, while we retired to the kitchen. Loud guffaws from Menya and Grace.... A B.M. sneaked up on her. By the time we got her to the commode, she had already begun without us. We cleaned up her clothes and sheets and got her onto the commode chair for a successful conclusion. She was in no way disturbed by her loss of control. But the transfer seemed harder than a week ago. *Happy birthday Pete!* [Pete's birthday was the following day.]

Friday December 29, evening, Roben
Lots of people here, lots of love, voices of children. The house seems cheerier than last night. But it only lasts so long. Menya becomes withdrawn and inconsolable for a while. Doesn't want music or company. Pete made some food that she had none of. When she was ready for company, I read her some Harry Potter. Menya began asking

for something I couldn't fathom. I wondered if she was finally going to tell me where the gold was buried. She said, 'Yes! yes…I…it…' and then made a huge production of dying, which involved flailing of limbs, rolling of eyes and some deeply unconvincing gagging noises. I told her she'd never win an Oscar. She growled. Then she began to reach for something. After discovering that it wasn't her teddy bear, my hand or her water bottle, I began to hand her random objects from around the room—kleenex boxes, empty chocolate containers, books, CDs. We had a good laugh, but none of these things was what she wanted. She cheerfully refused her night meds and after an unsuccessful trip to the commode, we both slept a few hours.

Saturday December 30, early afternoon, Jen W.
Menya woke peacefully to a house with June [weekend homemaker], Joan (the VON nurse), Pete, Morris and me. Despite serious communication problems—her 'yes'-es and 'no's aren't clear any more—we gave Menya a back rub and change of shirt, some mouth care, and some drugs. I think it helps to remind her that it's best to stay ahead of the pain. Dilantin was a hard sell. I think she understands that she will have seizures without it, but it isn't easy for her to swallow pills any more.

Marg at Helena's

29/12 Fri   2 smshot
             Lge · BM @ 1800hr.
11 pm refused all meds, godamit, and so cheerfully so.

7:45 2 dilaudid, 2 @ 5 tylanol, 1 HUGE cranberry juice pill

30-12 Saturday

1:30PM   2nd Dilaudid — easily convinced
         + 2 Dilantin — but not more
         — seemed difficult to swallow

3:00PM mixed 2 Dilantin w ice cream
        + took them, though it was AWFUL
        ☹ BLEAAHHHRGH!!

NURSE JOAN WANTS US TO GET
MENYA to TAKE 8 DILANTIN A
DAY TO PREVENT SEIZURES.

9pm BM
Menya refused bedtime meds, so only 6 dilantin today

Sun Dec 31
        3am leg pain ⇒ 2 Dilaudid, 2@5 Tylenol   Refused sleep meds

        3:30PM 8 Dilantin!! ☺
        18h-19h BM
        19h25 1 dilaudid
        23:00 30 rzepam, 2mg Dilaudid, 2@5 Tylenol, 4 Valium, 4mg Ativan

From the Green Book

*Saturday December 30, afternoon, Alina**
Friends were taking care of Menya when I arrived. When they left, Pete spent some time with her. Then for the next two hours, Menya tried to tell me something and I tried to guess. She said it wasn't physical but emotional. And she cried. The only words I understood were, 'I can't.'

*Sunday December 31, morning, Nancy**
Menya and I talked, as much as she could, quietly, for about an hour and a half. Among the things she said were that she was sad, angry, confused and she 'can't do this'. Joan, the VON nurse, and Jinn [weekend homemaker] arrived and we got her feeling a bit more human. Had a good cry and then seemed calmer afterwards. Carla and Jen arrived.

Sunday December 31, late afternoon, Morris
Reading and experience tell me that the dying often attempt to express the inexpressible and can't find the words. This can result in frustration for both the patient and the caregiver. I don't respond to Menya's saying 'I can't' by trying to guess. I gently caress her forehead and try to calm her that way.

CHAPTER FIVE
January 2001

Monday January 1, overnight, Jen W.

Arrived to relieve Margaret [an old family friend from Montreal]. Once again there was a B.M. accident, necessitating a complete bed change, warm water wash, etc. Menya wasn't too disturbed by this and I assured her that I wasn't. Later she asked to try the commode again. I was quite proud of my smooth one-person transfer but then on the way back, her legs buckled, and we slid gracefully to the floor. No damage to anything but pride. Pete helped Menya back onto the bed; I worry about his back. Menya listened happily to some Harry Potter, making appropriate fearsome sound effects for the dementor's appearance. After a while, she asked for quiet and tried to sleep.

Tuesday January 2, evening, Morris
Team meeting

June circulated the schedule for the next two weeks. The Room at the Inn program at the Royal York had worked well. Jen, Ben, and their families had used the hotel as a base. Menya's general condition has been better in recent days, perhaps as a result of the family visit. She is more alert and able to express herself better. Her appetite has improved somewhat and she has been drinking more.

We discussed the emotional strain on all of us of the ups and downs of Menya's condition. Saying goodbye over and over again is hard. Pete needs the occasional night away from home; the Room at the Inn program is available to him. An RN will now be added to the team to cover nights that Pete is away. Menya is losing bowel control. Diapers will be ordered and a training session held to cover diaper changing and other intimate care needs. Menya has decided to discontinue Decadron entirely, which may help account for her increased alertness. But she still needs to be encouraged to take eight Dilantin a day because seizures may occur more frequently now. There is no need for her to experience pain—ever. If she can't take pain meds orally or is in a coma, there are other ways of managing her pain. If she falls, we shouldn't be trying to lift her alone; it's best to keep her calm, as warm and as comfortable as possible, and to call for help.

*Wednesday January 3, morning, Sue M.**
Arrived to find Menya asleep. Unfortunately, the bed was soaked. The drainage bag was on the bed and virtually empty. Faye and I got her up and the bed changed. THH will see if they can get the VON nurse to come sooner. Menya is in great form today. She laughed when I suggested she needed a ballerina's pointe shoe to make her turning easier when she gets up. The nurse came and changed the catheter. Menya is resting comfortably now.

Thursday January 4, afternoon, Jennifer M.
Menya is restless…moving her legs a lot but doesn't appear to be wanting anything. Her friend Fiona arrived at 3:30 for a visit and they chatted. She suddenly became very restless. Pete put her on the commode. No results. Lying down again, Fiona and I massaged her head and feet. She was happy for about five minutes then started getting up and down, up and down. Carla and her sister Linda arrived and sat with Menya. Eventually she worked herself up to the top of the bed and sat on a chair. She's determined and couldn't be convinced to get back in bed…. Maybe it's a

good thing to be what we think of as stubborn when so many options have been lost.

Friday January 5, morning, Randi
Faye discovered that Menya's bed was wet—more catheter woes. Shortly after the VON nurse left, there was another leak. She came back and inserted another new catheter. We listened to a Dylan Thomas CD. Some tears and frustration. Menya kept saying, *'I can't leave'* but we couldn't get to what she meant. I asked her to draw how she was feeling. We got the sketch pad and pastels out; she seemed to enjoy making delicate marks on the paper.

Friday January 5, afternoon, Sue B.
Menya still saying, 'I can't leave' and 'I can't go on.' She delivered a long monologue this afternoon. Regrettably, I couldn't understand it except for the above-mentioned phrases.... What's a poor friend (especially a non-telepathic one) to do? I listened, wiped tears away, and we held hands.

Friday January 5, evening, Johanna*
She was awake and in good spirits—alert and responsive. I talked of my trip to visit friends in Georgia, of the beauty of the landscape, and a party that was held for refugees

from Liberia and Mauritania. She appeared interested, nodding and making appropriate sounds. Life can require a fair degree of courage and resilience, whether we're up for it or not.

Saturday January 6, early afternoon, Morris
Menya subdued. Repeating the words 'I can't.' Apart from quietly saying, 'When you're ready,' a couple of times, I didn't respond. I caressed her forehead. She ate a few grapes and said 'yes' to some harp music.

Saturday January 6, afternoon, Alina*
Menya was sad. She wanted to get up and go outside so Pete and I moved her in the wheelchair to the open doorway, wrapped in blankets. She sat there for about half an hour. When we moved her to the bed, she started to cry. I stroked her hair and wiped away the tears. Whenever I stopped, she would become emotional. So I began again. I did it for an hour and a half. My arm hurts but it definitely made her feel better.

Sunday January 7, evening, Roben
Found Menya chipper and responsive. Would seem to want something and then get confused. I told her it's okay

if she's confused; she's got a better excuse than most. She sat on the edge of her bed as I tried to guess what she wanted. It was something about music. Finally, I asked if she wanted one of her harps. She said, '*Yes!*' then seemed to hesitate. She grinned nervously and flexed her hand. 'I can't,' she said. 'You can't play it?' I asked. She shook her head sadly. 'Me neither,' I muttered in dramatic despair. She laughed. (I'd promised her that I would learn to play it but haven't begun.) I get some serious tsk-ing in response. Read some Harry Potter. Carla visited, followed by some friends. Generally a good mood in the house tonight.

Monday January 8, morning, Randi
Menya was awake when I arrived. She was rather sweaty and uncomfortable so I helped to freshen her. Change of clothes, sponge bath, lotion, powder, foot massage and manicure. She took her meds readily. The morning was quiet, with a candle and some music. Heather came for therapeutic touch—always good. As I write, Menya, with Faye's assistance, is standing up and down at the side of her bed.

Wednesday January 10, late evening, Pete
Read a few chapters of Harry Potter, then Menya had a B.M. and sent me away. Earlier she'd told Carla that I don't

love her and took her wedding ring off with her teeth. It's sitting on her bedside table.

Thursday January 11, morning, Randi
The bed was wet. Menya's alert but seems bothered and defensive today—upset about the wedding ring. [Faye had gently chided her for having removed the ring and urged her to put it back on. Menya was angered by Faye's attempted intervention.]

Thursday January 11, afternoon, Jennifer M.
Menya was agitated when I arrived and lay in bed clutching my hand. Her arm was trembling. I asked Faye if she'd had a seizure. Menya overheard and loudly said, 'No!' but I think she may be having mini seizures. I took a few minutes to read about the last few days; when I went back to sit with her, she was more agitated and pulled the covers over her head. I asked if she'd like me to go to the kitchen so she could have privacy. 'Yes!' she said. I left her alone, telling her to call if she wants me. Claudette [VON nurse] came; Menya wouldn't let her do anything so she didn't stay long. Then Menya called out for me to sit with her again, which I did. But just as suddenly, she began saying, 'Leave, leave.' Morris arrived and Menya agreed to his suggestion that she

sit in the wheelchair by the open door, to get some fresh air and hear the outside world. We wrapped her up in blankets and scarves, etc. She stayed there for more than an hour. Pete brought her in eventually, concerned that she was getting too cold. Menya was in a bad mood. 'No! No! No!' to everything. Eventually Pete helped her back into bed.

Friday January 12, morning, Randi
Menya refused food and medication. She's asserting her power to say, 'No'. She did, however, consent to listening to the CDs of her playing and singing. I said that she seemed to be on strike. Is she angry? 'Yes.' At me? 'Yes.' At Faye? 'Oh, yes!' About the discussion yesterday? 'Yes.' I apologized for whatever I may have done to offend her and assured her that Faye was sorry for upsetting her. Flash: Nichola [a complementary therapist] just arrived— nice surprise—a Reiki treatment.

Saturday January 13, afternoon, Alina*
When I arrived, Menya had had an accident. Pete cleaned her up and she got back in bed. She didn't want water or food but wanted to talk…. All I could understand was 'feel rage'. She repeated the word 'rage' for about five minutes; the more she said it, the more upset she got.

Sunday January 14, morning, Nancy*

When Pete came home, Menya pushed him away, shrugging off his touches. I tried to persuade her to express her anger while he was there, working with the image of a big block of rage impeding where she wants to go. Made some progress here, I think, with Pete talking to Menya. VON nurse came, then a therapeutic touch therapist.

Monday January 15, morning, Randi

Menya is fairly calm today, although still hostile toward Faye, which is distressing. We'll see how it works out. She has not wanted food or drink. She enjoyed being read to from *Gilgamesh* and had a good laugh at my pronunciation of Uta-napishti. (Well, you try it.)

[*Gilgamesh* tells the story of a Babylonian king, who, full of bravado, believes he can find the secret of eternal life. It is only after hearing the counsel of the demi-god Uta-napishti that Gilgamesh sadly accepts the fact that like all of humankind, he is mortal.]

Tuesday January 16, morning, Randi

She seemed more disoriented this morning.... Candace [VON nurse] took a lot of time on catheter maintenance, as it seemed to be the source of much irritation. Her leg has been bothering her more today. Candace stressed the importance of drinking more in order to alleviate her catheter woes.

Tuesday January 16, evening, Morris
Team meeting

June circulated the schedule for the next two weeks. Randi reported on Menya's treatment of Faye. Alina talked about how badly she felt about not knowing what to do when Menya repeated words such as 'rage' and 'help.' Jennifer M. was afraid there was something personal in Menya's asking her to leave. Pauline [the psycho-social worker] told us that despite our best efforts, we're not going to be able to satisfy all of Menya's needs. We need to accept and understand that our just being there helps.

We speculated that Menya had consciously decided to stop eating and drinking. If that's the case, the supervising nurse told us, the feeling of thirst will diminish as her body shuts down and prepares for death. Our emphasis as caregivers should now more than ever be on comfort measures. Menya will need regular diaper changes as a result of leakage around the catheter. Transfers to and from the commode will be increasingly difficult. Mouth care will be more important. Ice chips might help with her dry mouth. We also need to watch for bedsores. Bolsters and pillows under her knees and behind her back can help keep her comfortable.

Menya will likely be in an 'altered state of consciousness' much of the time now. We need to assure her that she's surrounded by love and that she is safe.

June raised the possibility of Menya moving to a palliative care unit. Were this to happen, the team shouldn't view it as a failure. There are times when a person's care becomes too intensive for the home, she said. Should Menya decide to transfer to a palliative care unit, she could have her own room. The team could continue to function as it has. Her bedding and personal belongings would come with her. The cats could visit. The only difference would be that palliative care nurses would be doing the physical caregiving. I left the meeting certain that Menya still wanted to die at home.

Wednesday January 17, morning, Sue M. *

Pete is a genius at helping Menya figure out what she needs. So patient. She agreed to let me do mouthcare. Also gave her hands and face a quick 'paw and whisker.' Did pericare. Officially won the 'village idiot' award by trying to help Menya to the commode by myself. We ended up sitting on the floor for an hour. It took Faye, the VON nurse, and me to get her back in bed. I told her she was free to fire me. [Menya's catheter difficulties were continuing. She was eating less and most of her liquid intake was now in the form of ice chips.]

Thursday January 18, afternoon, Jennifer M.
Restless and seemed unhappy when I arrived but quickly settled down. I massaged her feet, hands, and head. It felt good to be able to soothe her. Nichola arrived and gave her a Reiki treatment, after which she slept. When she awoke, we listened to music. Menya wanted me to read to her. Got halfway through a Kipling story, when she grew restless and I realized she needed a diaper change. After we got her back in bed, she held my hand and cried a little. I assured her she will be loved and cared for no matter what.

Thursday January 18, late evening, Pete
Menya made it clear that she does want to go into a hospice. Apparently, she's been trying to tell us this for some time…. With the decision, a lot of her general anger seems suddenly to have dissipated.

[I was surprised by her decision. Several of us asked her in different ways whether she was sure that that's what she wanted. There was no doubt that it was. Her decision meant that THH would now attempt to find her a bed. But that might take time.]

Friday January 19, overnight, Roben
Pretty good evening. We spent much of the time holding hands, with her talking. I tried to read her face and tone more than the words. I offered to wash her hair and she accepted. Even though I tried to be gentle around the scars on her head, she still experienced pain. She said the pain was new and her head did seem more swollen. [Without Decadron to slow its progress, her brain was swelling.] Bouts of pain through the night. She kept declining offers to reposition. Finally, because of a soiled bed, it became a necessity around 6 a.m. Note to everyone: When she's taken all her meds and has then been repositioned and that still doesn't help, ice cream is the answer.

Saturday January 20, evening, Pete
Just as Alina was leaving, Menya started having a weird seizure. She kept saying 'No, no, no' and couldn't stop. Sometimes it changed to 'Yes, yes, yes' (though not in a Meg Ryan way). The whole thing lasted an hour. There have been echoes of it throughout the evening.

Sunday January 21, morning, Nancy*

Spent a good two hours working with Menya's anger, again using the image of a block of rage. I suggested that instead of smashing her way through it, that she imagine herself stepping around it. I said she should try to get in touch with that part of herself that loves her.

Monday January 22, morning, Randi

A quiet morning. Menya wanted a hand to hold for much of the time. I read to her from *Gilgamesh* (she never seems to tire of it, nor do I). She ate a few strawberries. Has not taken any meds.

Tuesday January 23, evening, Roben

Arrive to see Pete and Menya holding hands—a nice sight. She had some grapes. I read a bit of *Gilgamesh*, which I'd never read before. When it was over, I told her it was beautiful and powerful, but a bummer. She laughed.

Wednesday January 24, morning, Morris

Arrived late morning. Menya quiet but not peaceful. Shakes her head in frustration. I caress her forehead and she dozes a bit. I'm having trouble adjusting to her decision to move to a palliative care facility. A sense that somehow we've let her down, haven't done what we all agreed to. *But*, I remind myself, we also agreed that Menya was in charge and I don't doubt that she now wants to be on a palliative care ward.

[Even at this late stage we were still getting advice from well-meaning people who knew exactly how to save Menya. For example, they'd heard of a woman with terminal cancer who had been cured by a Polish doctor who had put her on a diet of dandelion roots brewed in fresh—and the key was *fresh*—goat urine.]

Thursday January 25, morning, Randi
When I arrived, Pete was trying to relieve the pain in Menya's leg. I tried applying the 'magic bag' and some gentle manual pressure from foot to thigh. The heat seemed to provide some comfort.

I settled in to massage her foot and put on some Loreena McKennitt. I danced around to it a bit, to get my energy going. (If passers-by looked in, they might have thought I was doing some kind of belly dance healing ritual.) Then I invited Menya to sit on the side of the bed so I could scratch her back and give it a rub.

She was agreeable to the idea of a wash up, so I gave her the full treatment, including pericare and mouth (she brushed her teeth herself). As I write, 12:50 p.m., Menya is feeding herself a 'pizza pop', eyes half closed, listening to harp music.

Thursday January 25, afternoon, Jennifer M.
Menya was sleeping peacefully for about half an hour when I arrived. When she awoke…I gave her a long foot and hand massage, which she clearly enjoyed—lots of sighs and smiles.

She's having trouble keeping her left leg on the bed. She pushes it off on purpose and then can't lift it back up. We listened to music and held hands. While Carla visited, I stayed in the kitchen, composing fridge magnet personal ads….

Friday January 26, morning, Randi
It's a 'No' day, a hide under the covers day. But there was an audible chuckle from under the covers when I put on the first strains of the P.D.Q. Bach CD. And there was some relief for Menya when the VON nurse came. Relief from the tension and bad feelings generated by her unrelenting rejection of Faye, who is on the brink of quitting. Menya says 'No' to just about every indication that Faye is in the house. This makes me feel wretched too.

2:30 p.m. It's been an emotionally difficult day for all of us. Faye quit after saying goodbye and wishing Menya peace and love. I feel resentful of her treatment of Faye. I know I have to get some distance—the weekend will help. But these hours alone with her today are strained. I told her that I was (and am) upset by how she treated Faye, that I'll need time to get over it, and that she can ask me to leave, too, if she needs to. Having witnessed her turning on Faye, I'm aware it's not out of the question.

This is getting ridiculous.... I'm already feeling a bit better. I shook hands with Menya.... It seems she doesn't want to dismiss me, nor I her for that matter.

Friday January 26, evening, Roben

Restless, pained and once again refusing meds. Tonight as Pete was leaving, she wanted him to do something. By process of elimination, over the course of half an hour, we deduced that she wants to move back upstairs until space becomes available in a palliative care facility. She was quite agitated. 'Menya,' I said, 'I respect your decision to go back upstairs, but the three of us aren't strong enough to get you there.' She seemed to relax once a we're-all-in-this-together tone was adopted, but remained adamant about going back upstairs.

with Margaret about tomorrow, Menya seemed
quite adverse to me making the call until
I phrased it as a non-clarinet courtesy.
She's quite a moral woman, this one.
After some pain killers and ativan she
dozed for awhile. Her left foot kept falling
off the bed — she is now unable to pull it
up by herself — so I placed a pillow on the
wooden chair and nudged it up against
the bed so her foot would end up there and
not dangling, likely so:

Slept until about 2:30, then woke and let me
know she was wet. I got the comod chair ready
and a fresh nightie, just in case, as well as
a fresh blue pad (the substantial ones) and
diaper. Once we got her sitting up, however,
she gauged that she would be unable to stand.
I thought about changing her while she sat,
but that was ridiculous. I tucked what I
could of the souled pads and such under her and
changed her nightie (clothes on the washer).
Then we lay her back down in bed and got
ready to roll her in bed. I flattened the bed
but she had some seizures from the effort and
we waited for those to pass. I brought her
right hand up on her chest so she wouldn't
lay on it and asked her to reach at for

From the Blue Book

I suspect she might want a real bath. There doesn't seem to be anything else—privacy's not a concern, nor is noise, nor the arrangement of her bed. I think she's just fucking bored. I would be too.

Menya's left foot kept falling off the bed as she dozed. I placed a pillow on a wooden chair and nudged it up against the bed so her foot would end up there. She slept until 2:30 a.m., then let me know she was wet. I got the commode chair ready and a fresh nightie, as well as a fresh blue pad and a diaper. Once we got her sitting up, however, she realized that she wouldn't be able to stand.

[Here followed a two-page, detailed and illustrated description of changing the bed and Menya all by herself. At the end of her description, Roben added: 'If this were the cooking channel, I would now pull out a pre-changed Menya, prepared in advance.']

Monday January 29, morning, Randi
Menya expressed discomfort throughout the morning but refused pain meds. She was too weak to transfer to the commode, so I washed her and changed her bedclothes as she sat on the side of the bed. The effort involved in changing her and doing pericare really tuckered her out. Tammy [a new homemaker] came at 11, and did mostly

housekeeping things. As I get ready to leave, Pete is attempting to give Menya some pain meds.

Tuesday January 30, afternoon, Linda*
When I arrived Menya was asleep. After she awoke, we chatted and she seemed calmer than I'd seen her in a while. The people in the Palliative Care Unit [at St. Michael's Hospital] called and said a bed would be available in the morning. I forwarded the message to Pete's cell phone. Menya tried to sit up with my help but neither of us had the strength to get her up.

Now listening to Menya singing and playing the harp. Beautiful.

Tuesday January 30, evening
Team meeting
Randi described how hard the last week had been as a result of Menya's treatment of Faye. Faye spoke of how important her relationship with Menya had been to her and of her deep sadness about what had happened. Other members of the team expressed their regret too. Pauline [the psycho-social worker] reminded us that Menya is in charge; that's our agreement. At times she will make foolish decisions, but we must honour them.

Pete reported that he'd had a call offering Menya a private room in the Palliative Care Unit (PCU) at St. Michael's Hospital. Menya had accepted and would be transferred the next morning. An ambulance would be at the house at 8 a.m. Pete said he was happy about the move—he could be a husband. Menya could have real baths. The house could return to being a home. We agreed that the team schedule should remain as is but that we would meet in a week to re-evaluate it. Menya should be settled into her new routine by then and might want—or need—shorter visits.

Pauline addressed the feelings of failure some of us might be feeling. We were now moving from the ideal of recent months—palliative care at home—to what was now best, care on a palliative care ward. We needed to support Menya's decision. We began to talk about the ways in which each of us had been transformed by the experience of caring for Menya. Roben said that it was the most worthwhile thing she'd ever done. Pauline urged us to try to hold on to what we'd learned.

Wednesday January 31, 4:30 p.m., Pete
Menya moved into the PCU today! It's a big relief and Menya seems happy about it. I spent the afternoon hold-

ing her hand and reading to her. She seemed relaxed. I hung up the photo of her playing her harp.

Wednesday January 31, 6:30 p.m., Marjeiry
[Marjeiry and Menya were members of the same dragon boat team.] Menya looked calm and relaxed when I arrived. I got a smile from her. We joked around, me doing the talking, of course. She said she felt happy and that this was what she wanted. I read a few pages of *The Princess Bride*. She drank a lot of water and had some grapes, but refused dinner. She kept dozing off as we held hands.

CHAPTER SIX
February 2001

Thursday February 1, morning, Randi
Menya appears to be comfortable in her new bed and sur-
roundings. I fed her some breakfast. One of the nurses
went to get a fresh hot muffin. As we waited for it, Menya
did some 'mime' eating, and quite convincing she was. I was
holding her hand and she gestured as if she were taking a
piece of food, putting it in her mouth, and chewing it. This
cracked me up. Although I laughed, she was thoroughly
convinced she was eating something. She's been tugging
at the grey push button pinned to her clothes—I assume
it's a buzzer for the nurse—and put it in her mouth a few
times, out of curiosity, I guess. *Menya had a real bath! Yay!*
Ate lunch. She was moved to another room.

Thursday February 1, afternoon, Jennifer M.

Menya was sleeping deeply when I arrived. She looks both comfortable and very tired. I'm thrilled to read that she had a bath! No doubt this has tired her out. Her room is nice. I'm a bit surprised it's a double room, but she is the only one here. Oops, spoke too soon. Menya's room-mate has just arrived, an older woman who can still walk a little, with a small entourage. The patient's doctor carried on a loud conversation, which woke Menya. She was groggy. Played some harp music and gave her a foot and hand massage. Lots of big smiles. Nichola arrived at 3:30 and gave her a Reiki treatment. Menya indicated that she wanted to sleep, so I gave her a provisional goodbye kiss.... She seems quite content and peaceful. The nurses wanted to know about Menya's team, so I showed them this log.

5:30 p.m. I'm leaving a little early as Carla is here and Menya is still fast asleep. I'm so happy that she is comfortable and seems content. Love to all.

Friday February 2, morning, Randi

Groundhog's Day, if anyone gives a hoot. Menya was awake but groggy when I arrived. The nurse was giving her a sponge bath. I gave Menya a couple of bites of scrambled eggs, which the nurse very kindly prepared in place of the cold rubbery french toast on the tray. Menya dozed off in mid-bite. I've been sitting by her side as she sleeps through people to-ing and fro-ing. Marjeiry [who works at St. Michael's Hospital] stopped by for a visit. The supervising doctor looked in on Menya. He observed that she's been sleeping a lot since her arrival and in his opinion, it's the progression of the disease. Menya stirred toward the end of my visit, and sipped some water, swallowing it with difficulty. I held her hand and serenaded her for a while. She smiled now and then. Right now she's fondling her amber necklace. She's taken a couple of bites of a tuna sandwich, chewing very slowly, very....

Friday February 2, afternoon, Pete
Menya sleeping a lot.... Maybe she's ready now.... I held her hand, and she squeezed it. At some level she understands. At another she doesn't. I'm finding it hard to let go of being a caregiver, of worrying about this and that.

Friday February 2, overnight, Roben
I apply some moisturizer to her shoulders, which seem itchy. Find soapflakes behind one ear and remove them, massaging lotion into her ears. Menya smiles. She is moving in and out of sleep. She clutches her amber. Leigh [a

high school classmate, now a nurse] drops by. Words fail her and we sit quietly, sharing the space. I intercept and embrace her before she leaves.

In her sleep Menya furrows her brow and frowns sometimes; at other moments, she smiles (a wry, half mouth smile) and nods as if sharing sorrows and jokes. She seems so much more at peace and nearer the end than last week…. The nurses come in and turn her, a cheerful and competent crowd. The three of them make it so easy on Menya, she hardly wakes. A helluva lot better than me grabbing both sides of the transfer sheet and yanking her about. I'm tired and have clearance from the good woman to go. I'm not worried about her. She has better care than we were able to provide at home. I promised her in September I wouldn't cry around her 'coz this is her time, but I broke that promise tonight….

Saturday February 3, morning, Roben
It's morning and I'm back. Felt like a coward for not staying last night. The change was so profound that I started to freak out. Better I left. She is sleeping, clutching a bear. There is fresh moisturizer on her lips. Her breathing has taken on a halting quality and a deep sea sort of sound—fluid in the lungs? It sounds more pronounced than snor-

ing and has a pattern—two breaths in, one out, and then a pause of ten to fifteen seconds. She doesn't seem troubled in the slightest by this, so I won't be either. Her expression is relaxed and contented. I am delighted at the quality of care that she is getting here. I stop one of the nurses to tell her that. A nurse came by and spoke of suctioning Menya before her jacuzzi to get rid of the fluid in her lungs....
They don't call it suctioning for nothing; that thing really sucks. They took pity on me and let me help with bathing Menya. Such pleasure on her face. The flannel sheet they brought for her body and towel for her head were warm and soft from the dryer.

Saturday February 3, afternoon, Morris
Menya sleeping peacefully but with raspy breathing. Reminds me of my mother's breathing before she died. Wonder if part of Menya's motivation in choosing to come here was that she could more easily let go, more easily detach herself from us, and from life. Maybe it wasn't Menya clinging to life so much as our clinging to her.

Sunday February 4, morning, Roben
After a shot of meds to help out with her lungs, she fell deeper into sleep. They suctioned her again and the

quality of her breathing changed but not the quantity of breath taken in. She is breathing like someone not long for it. They wash and turn her. She sleeps. Margaret, a nurse I've not seen before, comes in quietly and rubs my shoulder, saying she didn't want to startle me. She asks about my relationship with Menya and if she's married, how her husband is and if she has small children. The care does not stop with physical care here. Fine people.

Sunday February 4, morning, Nancy*
Had to miss my shift last weekend and was looking forward to seeing Menya. I wasn't prepared for such a dramatic change. Thankfully, Roben was here when I arrived to cushion my shock—and my grief. Menya seemed to be dozing intermittently. I offered to give her a foot massage, at which point she ripped back the covers to expose her feet. I took that to mean, yes, she'd love a foot massage. A little visualization—tried to imagine the ventilation system as the sound of a waterfall in a beautiful wood, warm, with birds singing.

Sunday February 4, afternoon, Ian
[Ian was a friend and former neighbour.] I recall a conversation with Menya back in September. Between tears

and laughter, we talked about what happens when you die. She knew my [Christian] beliefs but said she thought that when you die, it's like that magical moment when a drop of water hits the surface of the ocean. At that moment, there is only peace and knowledge—every question is answered—and you're in harmony with the universe. What a wonderful way to look at death. It's not the end, only part of the journey.

*Sunday February 4, afternoon, Johanna**

Had the privilege of sitting with Ian. Around her Menya has drawn the people she needs and who so clearly love her. Her breathing is deep and mucousy, with momentary pauses. She lies peacefully, we stroke her forehead, hold her hand and voice words we hope are reassuring to her—and to us.

The nurses have turned her, put lotion on her arms and hands, cream on her lips and brushed her hair.

Sunday February 4, evening, Morris

Menya breathing more easily. Briefly alert enough to acknowledge my presence and my telling her that Jen and Ben and their families would soon be here. She's been reaching for an imaginary drink, bringing it to her mouth and sipping. Nurses just rearranged the bed, turned Menya and did mouth care.

Monday February 5, morning, Randi
When I arrived at 9 a.m., Menya was being washed. I waited in the other room as they suctioned her lungs. They've suctioned her twice this morning and given her an injection to help dry up her rattling lungs. As I sit beside her bed—it's noon—the congestion has increased again.... I sang softly to her for a while and read her web page to her—it was my first time seeing it. [We had printed out some of the material on Menya's web site so that the nurses, doctors and volunteers on the PCU could read it.] Eventually she dozed and slept for an hour and a half.

12:30 p.m. The doctor looked in and said they're battling the fluid build up, though not with much success. In her semi-comatose condition, she no longer has the normal reflex to eliminate the lung fluids that gather naturally.

Monday February 5, afternoon, Ian
Arrived to find Menya sleeping, looking quite peaceful. Carla arrived and they spent some quiet time alone. Later in my visit, Menya was alert; we 'talked,' even laughed a

February 2001

little. She knows I'm going on retreat for two days (big frown) but smiled when I told her I'll be back on Thursday. She even waved goodbye as I left. Wonderful tears flowed down my cheeks as I walked slowly home.

Tuesday February 6, morning, Randi
Here for about an hour and a half. A few hand squeezes from Menya. Though still rattly, her breathing is more peaceful and she continues to appear quite comfortable. I've been softly singing a stream of consciousness 'top forty' of Menya's and my favourite hits. A nurse came in for a brief visit, freshening and moistening Menya's mouth. She explained something of the body's natural anaesthetic taking over when one no longer eats or drinks.

Tuesday February 6, noon, Marjeiry
Spent my lunch hour with Menya, holding hands. I read her home page to her, commenting on her beautiful hair in one of the photos. [As part of her home page, Menya had created a 'Comb Page,' using photos to illustrate her adventures with her hair in recent years.] She's sleeping through all this, but occasionally I get a little squeeze from her hand. The 'raspy' breathing is there and she's resting calmly, hugging her bears.

Tuesday February 6, evening, Morris
Team meeting

June Galbraith said that we had accompanied Menya on her journey to this point but that soon she would be completing it on her own. We reflected on what Menya's loss was going to mean to each of us. Jennifer M. spoke of her sadness at seeing her slip away, combined with a sense that her agony would soon be over. Marjeiry described Menya as her coach, pushing her to her limit. Ben, whose wife is a midwife, spoke of the parallels between our coming into the world and leaving it, suggesting that we need midwives at both ends of life. I said the meetings of the care team were the best I'd ever attended. Our agenda was always clear: how could we best serve Menya as her condition deteriorated? how could we best help each other cope? The only thing we ever seemed to decide at academic meetings at the College where I taught was that we would meet again.

Pauline said that Menya had given each of us a gift, the sense that we will be richer for this experience. Menya's rapid deterioration in the palliative care unit, she thought, might be the result of having held on at home. Now she felt free to let go. I speculated on the motives that had brought our diverse group together. Some of us were rehearsing our own deaths, or making up for deaths past, when we felt we hadn't done enough. In caring for Menya we were working on ourselves. The emptiness of so much of life makes us hunger for meaning and for meaningful things to do.

*Wednesday February 7, morning, Sue M.**

What a difference a week makes…. Her breathing is *so* different from January 31, the big moving day. I think she knows I'm here and who I am. We hold hands for a bit. She is squeezing and stroking her soft brown teddy. She seems restless, moving her left leg, touching her lips, adjusting her nasal prongs. The staff here is wonderful.

Thursday February 8, morning, Randi

I came around 10 a.m. Menya smiled when I greeted her, which was lovely. Grace, Dr. John's wife, and Grace's mother, came in for a brief visit. A nurse suctioned Menya, after which she dozed. Then a Palliative Care Unit volunteer came to do Menya's nails. I said that I'd like to do them; it was something I enjoyed. Ben came and we chatted as I did the nails. I was watching to see if Menya was flinching, as I clipped, filed and cleaned. No flinching. Not even when I cut her thumbnail so short it bled. But she may not have noticed because it was her right hand. I recalled Menya's mischievous accusation, after she took a fall on the sidewalk—I was supposed to be helping her—that I was trying to kill her. Sorry, sweetheart.... I'm finding it hard to say goodbye.

[Randi, an actor and singer, was going to be performing out of town for the next ten days. She knew she wouldn't see Menya alive again.]

Thursday February 8, 10:15 p.m., Janet
There have been many people here all evening. Strong supportive vibes, with lots of distress running just underneath. *Roben turned thirty today*—and as usual brimming over with love and intuitiveness. Pete was alone with Menya for about an hour, while Ian, Roben and I hung out in the lounge.... Grief, peace and love abounded—all mixed with relief that she is in such good hands.

Friday February 9, 3:30 p.m., Ian
Arrived to find Menya's sister, mother and father visiting. Menya seems at peace. There was a small amount of commotion around the other bed. A nurse came into the lounge to tell us that the older woman in the next bed had passed away.... Morris and Carla went in to tell Menya.

Jen went to the piano and played. [Although the piano was in the lounge, it could be heard in the adjoining rooms, including Menya's.]

Friday February 9, overnight, Roben
Shortly after Jen left, Menya's breathing seemed to get worse again, so I sat her up and called for a nurse to suction her. The only resistance Menya offered (or indication that she was at all bothered) was to raise her *right* hand—yes, the one we haven't seen move in a while—toward her face.

Menya's roommate is gone, bare bed, bare spot in someone's life. Day before yesterday when I came in, Menya grabbed my wrist and forced my knuckles onto her chest. She was communicating affection. It was almost a primate gesture. Solid, earthy, loving. My Koko. I fell asleep holding her hand. Woke to find one of the night nurses had tucked me in with a flannel sheet.

Later a nurse comes in and asks if my mother [Menya] would like some ice water. I tell her that Menya is 36 and my friend, and 'Have you seen her web site?' I give her a crash course on Menya before I let her get the water, poor dear. The nurses have come to wash her; they ask me to take a little walk. Now I'm in the lounge. There is a large bunch of tiger lilies on the table. Some of the petals have begun to wrinkle and age; others are just opening. Some are adorned with pollen, others have lost their potency. Each flower lives, gives beauty, takes nourishment, grows old and helps nourish other flowers. But who mourns a flower? We understand that their passing is an integral part of life.

Saturday February 10, afternoon, Carla
This is the first time I have written here. I haven't been able—and still am not able—to find the words I need. But I do want to express my profound gratitude to all of you Menyans for your love and care of my girl, and for this record of a remarkable time and community. Blessings on all of you.

Saturday February 10, later that afternoon, Leigh
I am sitting with Menya talking to her about the cool things she did in high school. She and I and a few others were nerdy types. I didn't really know Menya much after high school until we reconnected when she was diagnosed and we ran into each other at Women's College Hospital. It wasn't difficult to pick up the banter and joking. All through her illness Menya has been brave, funny, and incredibly sensitive to others' feelings and reactions. I was

honoured to help care for her at Women's College and then to stand beside her as she married a wonderful man. I am honoured to have been her friend.

Saturday February 10, late night, Jen W.
Sister Jen here with the harp music and the quiet. I had Sarah McLaughlin on at first but it wasn't right. Menya is not responsive in any way today, though her eyes move in her dreams. I cherish this time alone with her, selfishly. I have been looking forward to it all day. I talked to her at first, cried buckets, and piled up the tissues. Then Ian and Glenn had time with her. Now I'm just sitting and watching. She probably needs time without all of us try-ing to say death-defyingly meaningful things. I wonder if she's in there, unable to respond, thinking, 'God, her hand is clammy,' or 'Can't a person get some rest around here?' The nurses have been in to check her vitals and swab her mouth. One nurse said that the last time she was in, a week ago, she had joked with Menya about a particu-larly dry anthropology text they had both been required to read. Menya had laughed about it—hard to believe. In my mind, I hear her voice demanding french toast.

You on the care team. You are amazing and generous spirits. I told Menya today what incredible people she had assembled around herself, and how I hoped we would all preserve the best selves that she had brought out in us. I'm going to stop writing and go hold her hand and gaze at her beautiful face. Tomorrow I go home and leave her in the strong hands of all you others who love her (tears to write that). What an experience this is and has been. Thank you all.

Sunday February 11, 10:20 a.m., Janet
Just as Ian was leaving to get to church and choir, I arrived. Unplanned. One of the nurses said it's always that way. We 'Menyans' seem to flow in and out as if 'by divine intervention.' There are terribly long pauses now between Menya's breaths but she does seem to be at peace. I have to go and work at my office this afternoon. If the end comes today, I'd be grateful for a call.

*Sunday February 11, later that morning, Nancy**
Arrived about 10:30. Beautiful, crisp winter morning with the sun streaming into Menya's room. Janet was here, singing to Menya. I had run into Pete on the streetcar Thursday morning; I don't believe it was a coincidence. I had been thinking that maybe I should stop in at the hospital before I went to work. In fact we both came. Pete suggest-

ed I have a few moments alone with Menya. Part of me was reluctant, the part that a hospice volunteer finds most difficult—letting go, saying goodbye. I said what I wanted to Menya and thanked her for allowing me into her life at this precious time. God knows I will miss her.

Sunday February 11, 3 p.m., Morris
I am alone with Menya. I sit holding her hand. Harp music now. Gregorian chant just before that. Jen, Brad and the kids are on their way back to Michigan. Ben, Felice and the kids are on their way in from Ottawa. Ben will stay now until Menya dies. A volunteer was in to do therapeutic touch. (It looks like conducting.) I'm conscious of Johanna's suggestion at the last caregivers' meeting about being present in every moment. There is this moment, now this moment, now this. Menya is breathing heavily but seems peaceful as she slowly slips away. Roben's gone back with Pete to choose some of Menya's favourite clothing to dress her in after she dies.

*Sunday February 11, evening, Johanna**
Stood and watched Menya sleep. It reminded me of all the nights I go into my daughters' room and watch them sleep. There is a restful beauty in it—no conversation, no strug-

gle to communicate imperfectly. Just the chance to look with love, uninterrupted.

Monday February 12, noon, Marjeiry
Popped in again at lunch time to share these last treasured moments, the little twitching of her thumb. Doctor explained the status of Menya's condition. Low pulse. No suctioning necessary. No visible response to my chatter. Just holding hands is enough.

Monday February 12, evening, Roben
Picked out some clothes with Pete yesterday—purples and reds for a royal lady. Also purple earrings, although I don't know if they'll work out. Got a brief smile this evening when I addressed her as 'my queen'. Her breathing is shallow, laboured and spare. I am amazed at how much a person can live through. Her countenance is relaxed and contented. She is beginning to collect the perfume of her state about her.

Monday February 12, 9:45 p.m., Morris
Nurses turned Menya. Skin duskier. Greater spaces between breaths. Temperature slightly elevated. More breakthrough meds. The end is getting closer. They say she

could go quickly and without a lot of warning. Ben will stay the night.

Tuesday February 13, 10 a.m., Ben

I came at 11 p.m. and sat with Menya for a while as she slept deeply. She seemed quite peaceful. I didn't see any responses from her at all. I drifted in and out of sleep. In the morning there seemed to be a subtle change. Menya's breathing is more gaspy, much more regular, as if something automatic is taking over from whatever level of consciousness is left. The nurses continue to say she could go at any time. It could be triggered by moving her or she could just slip quietly away. It's likely the end will come soon now. The morning nurse today was a little surprised that she was still here. Jen called and said a few words to Menya through the phone.

Tuesday February 13, afternoon, Ian

Menya is resting peacefully and although she's not responsive, I think she knows I am here. Pete, his mother Mary [who had just arrived from England], and Linda* arrived. We've been giving each other time alone with Menya. Her breathing has become more regular with little sighs after each breath. Now there are ten or twelve breaths, then a long pause before it all starts again. They have given Menya more pain medication. Her feet, legs, arms, and hands are cooling off. She is getting ready to go. We sit, stand, and wait lovingly by her side.

AT 5:20 P.M. MENYA took one last breath—and was gone. Ian, Linda and Mary were at her side. Pete, who had just left the hospital, Carla, Ben, Roben, Joy, and I arrived moments later.

The Palliative Care Unit had assured us that there was no need for hurry of any kind when Menya died. We could spend as much time with her as we wanted. I alerted the funeral home and told them we'd call again when we were ready. We called Jen, and left a message for Randi, who had been checking in daily. June Galbraith began informing the volunteers.

Roben, Linda and Joy, with the help of the nursing staff, dressed Menya's still warm body in the black skirt and burgundy batik top that had been chosen. They brushed her hair and put on lip gloss and a little perfume. Roben removed the amber necklace she had given Menya and replaced it with an amber pendant. As they'd agreed, Roben would toss the necklace into the sea, to symbolize Menya's return to nature.

We each spent quiet time alone with her and then did so as a group. When everyone was ready, I called the funeral home. Ben, Joy and I stayed behind after the others left. Two young men dressed in black arrived, carefully placed Menya's remains in a body bag and transferred it to a gurney, which they covered with a white cloth. Then a hospital employee, a man with the dignified bearing of a Buddhist priest, slowly, and silently, led us through various corridors in the bowels of the hospital to the waiting hearse. The gurney was rolled into the hearse, its doors were shut, and off it went.

We had sorted out the question of Menya's burial in December. Her body would have to be embalmed and stored in a vault not far from Castleton until spring. The biodegradable cardboard box she preferred could no longer be used; moisture would seep in and weaken it in storage. We chose a simple unfinished wooden box instead.

I accompanied the hearse taking Menya's remains to the vault. I asked the driver, Jason, an earnest young funeral director, if he would mind dressing down for the trip. He didn't mind and wore jeans and a sweatshirt. When we arrived at the vault, a couple of men wheeled Menya's casket into what looked like an underground wine cellar. Then Jason and I drove back to Toronto.

Tuesday February 20, evening, June Galbraith
Closing team meeting
The word 'closure' denotes an ending, a finality. Although a care team comes to an end, for many people it is a time not so much of ending but of transition—a time of grieving and loss, and a time of new beginning. With a special care team such as Menya's, we at Trinity Home Hospice have helped create a unique community, the ending of which requires a ceremony of its own. Even though care teams are disbanded, they live on in memory. If we meet a fellow care team member on the street months from now, we will remember a bar of Menya's favourite piece of music or a certain fragrance, …but we will remember.

So when Menya's team gathered for our closure meeting at Menya and Pete's, I could already sense a change. In the way we greeted each other with longer hugs; the empathy in our eyes; the hesitant laughter; and the mood of supportiveness that was felt but didn't have to be ar-

MENYA RUTH WOLFE

After an almost-five-year struggle with a rare breast cancer that spread to the brain and involved numerous surgeries, chemotherapies and other treatments, Menya Ruth Wolfe died in the Palliative Care Unit at St. Michael's Hospital on February 13, 2001 at the age of 36, surrounded by love. She leaves behind her remarkable husband, Pete Bevin, who shared the emotional roller coaster ride of her last years; her parents Carla McKague and Morris Wolfe; her siblings Jennifer and Benjamin; their partners Brad and Felice; and the nieces and nephews she so treasured: Noah, Emma, Graeme, Hannah and Paul. Menya began to tell her own story on her web site: www.menyawolfe.com. As well, she and her husband established a help page for other women living with inflammatory breast cancer: www.ibcsupport.org. Menya's family is grateful to the team of friends, volunteers, homemakers, nurses and doctors who lovingly cared for Menya at home for five months. Funeral for immediate family members.

A memorial service will be held at Hart House at the University of Toronto on Sunday March 4, 2001 at 1 p.m. In lieu of flowers, contributions in Menya's name can be made to Trinity Home Hospice, P.O. Box 324, Commerce Court Postal Station, Toronto, ON M5L 1G3. Menya also requested that donations be made to support research into Inflammatory Breast Cancer. In Canada: Saunders-Matthey Foundation for Breast Cancer Research, 13 Partridge Drive, Kanata, Ontario K2M 2P6.

ticulated. This gathering, I hoped, would give us a chance to express what the experience had meant to each of us; to celebrate Menya; to thank each other for our collective strength and support; and for those of us who work at THH to determine if there were things we could do better next time.

About fifteen people, friends, family and THH volunteers settled in around the coffee table. Candles were lit and we shared some of Menya's favourite treats that people had been kind enough to bring. I opened the meeting with an informal welcome, then invited anyone who wanted, to tell a Menya story. Everyone had a story. Funny and sad stories, recent stories and stories from some time back. There was music. There were tears and laughter. Warmth and love were expressed for Menya, Pete, and for each other. Then, following Pete's heart-felt thanks to the team, and my added thanks, there were more hugs, tears and laughter as people said goodbye.

So was this closure? In one sense it was, because for some of us this would be goodbye; the work of the 'team' was over. But giving of yourself to someone in this way, being there to care for them, is a profound experience you will always carry with you. You do not 'close' yourself to the experience or your memories. The bond that forms between the members of care teams is but one manifestation of the new life that springs from death and loss; it is part of the full circle of human experience.

CODA
Memorial Service and Burial

O N SUNDAY MARCH 4, 2001, we held a memorial service for Menya in a music room in Hart
House at the University of Toronto. Two hundred seats
were filled; another 150 people stood. Ben acted as host.
Music, both instrumental and vocal, was performed; stories were told. We even had a clown; Randi came as Njala
and brought the house down with her anecdotes and
songs, closing with: 'Today while the blossoms...', with
everyone joining in.

Two months later, on Saturday May 5, we buried Menya.
Her wedding ring, a stuffed cat (a gift from Roben), a letter
from Jen, and some drawings by her nieces and nephews
were buried with her. The service was non-religious and

informal. Several of us read. Jen sang. The kids scattered rose petals on the casket. At one point, someone's purse fell into the grave and had to be fished out using the handle of a shovel. We all threw or shovelled some earth onto the casket and then turned the rest of the job over to the professionals. By this time, the three youngest children had begun playing near the grave, a bittersweet reminder that life goes on.

Among the many letters and cards that arrived, the one that I think touched me most came from a friend whose 105-year-old aunt had recently buried an 80-year-old daughter. "Children shouldn't do such things to a parent," the aunt had said.

AFTERWORD
by Jeanette Browne
Volunteer Services Co-ordinator, Trinity Home Hospice

I F ANYONE HAD TOLD me ten years ago that I would be working in the health care field, I would have laughed. My impatience and squeamishness when it came to family illness, made it seem one of the last areas I might choose to work in. But life is strange. During a training program run by the United Way, I met Gloria Murrant, then the Coordinator of Volunteers at Casey House, a hospice in Toronto for men and women dying of AIDS. I learned a great deal about her work. Although I was still unnerved by the idea of my working in such a place, I was deeply moved by her commitment and compassion.

Not long afterward, I applied for a position at the newly established Hospice Association of Ontario (HAO).

The opportunity to develop a provincial organization devoted to helping new hospices begin their work intrigued me. In preparation for my interview, I went to see Gloria and once again I came away stirred by the importance of the work she was doing. I got the job. Looking back on it, what excited me most was being in on the ground floor of a movement that was questioning the way the medical establishment, and society at large, treated people who are dying. I now realize that not far below the surface was an awareness that my own parents were becoming increasingly frail, and that my brother and I would soon have to cope with their final illnesses and deaths.

The work at the HAO was extremely rewarding. I was part of a terrific team of people who were building something new and important. It was wonderful to see the kinds of services different hospices across the province were providing, each reflecting the needs of its community, and the values and experiences of its members.

HAO and a group of twenty hospices were originally funded by a generous five-year grant from the Trillium Foundation. Each year of funding was smaller than the previous one. In theory, the deficit was to be fundraised by each hospice. In practice, this was difficult. The time and skills necessary to fundraise were lacking among those whose first thought was care of their clients. Newer hospices didn't have access to Trillium funding and as their number grew, it became increasingly clear that new sources of financial support would need to be found.

The Hospice Association of Ontario and its members successfully lobbied the provincial government for on-going funds to support the training and education of pro-fessionals and volunteers. This funding continues through the Ministry of Health, Long Term Care Division. Thirty per cent of THH's budget comes from that source.

The longer I worked at HAO, the less squeamish I became about illness, death and dying. I came to see death as a natural part of the life cycle—something to hold in awe rather than be frightened by. Dying, I realized, presented opportunities for growth, intimacy and final reflections that can be experienced in no other way.

I told friends that if I were ever to work for a hospice, it would be Trinity Home Hospice. I loved the story of its inception, told so beautifully by June Callwood in *Twelve Weeks in Spring*, the simple story of people coming together to care for one of their own. I began to want to be closer to the 'real' work of palliative care, to leave what some regarded as an ivory tower job. As luck would have it, THH had created a new position of Volunteer Services Coordinator. I ripped the ad off the fax machine, and with some trepidation, sent in my résumé. I underwent a grueling interview, consisting largely of how I would respond to difficult cases and situations. I was hired and arrived at THH with eager anticipation in September 1997. During my first few months, I frequently heard colleagues say: 'Remember that case we talked about in your interview? Well, here's a similar problem and I need you to do something about it.' Once again I was excited by the opportunity to build something new (a volunteer services department), to work with people I liked and respected, and to see how well the advice I had been dispensing from my 'ivory tower' actually worked.

Over the years I've constantly been surprised by the diversity of the people who volunteer at Trinity Home Hospice. They come from all ages and stages of life. Some are students, struck by a desire to learn more about life (and death) and to be involved in something above the materialism of the society around them. Some are people who have been part of a positive experience in caring for family or close friends and wish to help others have a similar experience. Others believe that dying and death need to be celebrated in the same way that birth is. We all believe that living continues until death and that hospice care can help people recognize the value of their lives. Our volunteers are strong, committed people who are able to laugh and cry with their clients, who provide efficient care, and who are able, when necessary, to simply stay close and do nothing.

Let me tell a couple of stories that exemplify the kind of relationship that can develop. One of our volunteers, a woman in her sixties, was helping care for a young man in his twenties. He was dying of AIDS and no longer able to leave his home. As they talked, she learned that they both shared a love of the greenhouses in Allan Gardens (a park in downtown Toronto). Each of them went there, especially in winter, for quiet reflection. The young man said he wished he could go there one last time. The volunteer arranged for her son to videotape a tour of the greenhouse. On her next visit, the volunteer settled the young man in front of a VCR and took him on a tour of the greenhouse.

A young woman was dying of cancer. Her care team consisted of a large extended family, help from community professionals, and volunteers from THH. The woman was by now frail and bed-ridden but spoke constantly about wanting to go one last time to the family cottage near Peterborough. The family was frightened and resistant. The logistics would impossible to manage. What if she died while she was there? June Galbraith slowly convinced them that such a visit was possible. One member of the family had a large van. One of the community nurses volunteered to accompany the young woman. Arrangements were made with the local funeral home should she die during the expedition. At the cottage, she was able to be taken gently out into the water to float and look at the sky. Later, she lay in the grass and looked at the stars. Thus she said goodbye to a place that had been important to her. A few days after her return to Toronto, she died peacefully.

An idea that grew from a group of people helping a friend has become an amazing organization serving hundreds of clients every year. As Margaret Mead put it: 'Never doubt that a small group of thoughtful, committed citizens can change the world. Indeed it is the only thing that ever has.'

ACKNOWLEDGEMENTS

IT TOOK MONTHS before I could bring myself to begin work on this book. At first I tried to include too much. But I finally realized that what I wanted the book to do was simple—to walk the reader (and myself) through Menya's end of life story, from diagnosis to death, with a particular emphasis on the palliative care process. Like the filmmaker Allan King, who has said that he never quite understands a subject until he's made a film about it, I never quite understand an experience until I've written about it.

A number of people read and commented on the manuscript as it went through several drafts: Rick Archbold, Pete Bevin, John Blondal, Allison Bottomley, Jeanette Browne,

Dolores Cohnstaedt, Joy Cohnstaedt, Bronwen Cunningham, June Galbraith, Roben Goodfellow, Randi Helmers, Jennifer Mason, Beverly Matson, Marshall Matson, Carla McKague, Walter Mulkewich, Nancy Shepherd, Johanna Wall, Ben Wolfe and Jennifer Wolfe. I'm grateful to all of them for their comments and suggestions. They, of course, are not to blame for the decisions I ultimately took.

I'm grateful to June Callwood, who, at a time when her own plate was overflowing, took the time to read *Menya: An End of Life Story* and to write a moving introduction to the book. In a note agreeing to do the intro, she commented, "There is nothing in a lifetime that hurts more than the death of one's child. It is twenty years, four months and one day since our son Casey was killed and I still think of him every day, and miss him intensely."

My son, Ben Wolfe, a graphic designer, is responsible for the lovely look and feel of this book. Some of his typographic and design decisions are described on the copyright page.

More than anyone, I want to thank Joy Cohnstaedt for her unfailing love and encouragement.

ABOUT THE AUTHOR

M ORRIS WOLFE is a writer and editor. He taught part-time at the Ontario College of Art & Design between 1971 and 2001. Wolfe has written, edited, and co-edited eleven books, including: *A Saturday Night Scrapbook, Aurora: New Canadian Writing, Signing On: The Birth of Radio in Canada, Jolts,* and *OCA 1967-1972, Five Turbulent Years,* which was also published by grubstreet books. His essays, articles, reviews and columns have appeared in numerous Canadian magazines and newspapers. In 1994 he won a Canadian Association of Journalists Award for Investigative Journalism. A collection of his essays can be found on the grubstreet web site, www.grubstreetbooks.ca.

More of Menya Wolfe's Story on the Internet:

WWW.MENYAWOLFE.COM

Set up as a memorial, this site includes Menya's original home page (with photos from all stages of her life), her wedding site, a short piece she wrote about her illness in February 2000, a link to reminiscences posted by friends and family, and audio files of her harp music in MP3 format.

WWW.IBCSUPPORT.ORG

Menya and her husband Pete Bevin launched this inflammatory breast cancer information and support site in 1997. It remains active, offering disease and treatment information, references, personal stories, sign-up for the global IBC mailing list, and searchable archives of the list from January 2000 on.

WWW.MENYAWOLFE.COM/MEMORIAL.HTML
Menya's memorial service, held on March 4, 2001 at Hart House, University of Toronto, was recorded, and is here in MP3 format.

WWW.MCKAGUE.COM/PHOTOGRAPHS/SPECIAL/BANNERS/
Menya's aunt, Linda McKague van Will, created these memorial banners from some of Menya's favourite clothes and other personal effects, as keepsakes for family and friends.